GREAT PERSONALITIES
OF THE OLD TESTAMENT

Great Personalities of the Old Testament

THEIR LIVES AND TIMES

WILLIAM SANFORD LA SOR

FLEMING H. REVELL COMPANY

COPYRIGHT © MCMLIX BY FLEMING H. REVELL COMPANY

Westwood, New Jersey
London E.C.4—29 Ludgate Hill
Glasgow C.2—229 Bothwell Street

Library of Congress Catalog Card Number: 59-5500

Printed in the United States of America

1.1

To
JEAN L. LAMOREAUX
PAUL C. DOEHRING AND
ROGER K. NEVIUS
whose encouragement and inspiration
over the years have meant much to me
this work is affectionately dedicated

Preface

THE BIBLE IS a living book because it was wrought out in life. Moreover, it is a living book because it comes from the living God. I know of no other religious literature in which history and geography, in other words, men in time and space, are so essentially part of the religious ideas. Some would say that these other writings are "timeless." It would be more significant to say that the Bible speaks to living men in every life situation in every generation, because that is just the way it came into existence. Its God is the God who talked with men, acted on their behalf, loved them, and began a redemptive work which is necessary for every man in every earthly age. He is, as one has said, "God Who Acts." He is, moreover, God who speaks in order that His acts may be understood.

In past generations, Bible interpreters have studied the Biblical characters as "types." The spiritual and the allegorical meanings were the supremely significant meanings. More recently, scholars have subjected the Biblical characters to scientific study, and have either killed them or reduced them to historical curiosities. In the past few years, a generation of scholars has arisen that has protested in a soft-spoken way against this destruction of the spiritual values of the Bible by emphasizing the existential character of the Biblical scenes.

Without rejecting the spiritual and typological nature of the persons, events, and things in the Bible, without denying the value of critical study of the Biblical text and the application of scientific method, and without identifying myself with the existentialist school, I am attempting to study the Bible as it represents itself—or so I believe—namely, as the revelation that God made to man, at various times and in various ways, in real-life situations. In the following studies, I am attempting to recreate for myself and the reader the dimensions of reality in which God spoke, acted, used His particular servant, and so extended His redemptive revelation. I have attempted to make full use of the materials available to us in history, geography, cultural anthropology, psychology, and other branches of learning. I have not done this with any idea that I am above the Bible; rather, I have done it with the idea

7

that I want to be within the Bible. It is in this spirit that, while I have been willing to follow the methods of criticism, I have been unable to accept some of the extreme conclusions of criticism. Some may say, "The Bible by itself is enough for me." But what is the Bible? Disconnected details, or dead dogma, or the Book of Life? If I have been forced to reject the rationalistic form of criticism that is satisfied when it has dissected the Scriptures and labelled the parts, equally have I been forced to reject the dogmatic view that embalms the Bible and lays it out on the piano (or pulpit) for all to worship. The Bible is the Book of Life. It is that because it resulted from the experiences of living men with the living God, the God who wanted men to have life and to have it abundantly.

The studies were first presented to the men and women of the Chapel Bible Class in the Glendale Presbyterian Church, Glendale, California. For these beloved people, if I may accept their many statements to the effect, the Bible took on a new dimension of life. Through their generous gift of a tape recorder, it was possible to record the lessons and later to have them transcribed. Through the repeated encouragement of several of them, which at last was buttressed by the request of Dr. Frank S. Mead, Editor-in-Chief of Fleming H. Revell Company, these studies have been edited, revised somewhat, and put into printed form. I have tried, however, to retain the informality of the spoken word, for after all, God's Word was spoken before it was written.

If I may be permitted to extend that simile another step, let me say that it is my fervent prayer that what is now written will not return empty, but that it will lead to life. For when we get right down to basic facts, the Word of God was not given for our entertainment or our education, but for our salvation.

William Sanford LaSor

Altadena, California

Contents

Contents

GREAT PERSONALITIES
OF THE OLD TESTAMENT

CHAPTER I

Abraham: The Challenge

IN MANY WAYS, Abraham towers above all the other men of the Old Testament. He was the outstanding pioneer of a great pioneer people. Three great religions claim him as founder: Judaism, Mohammedanism, and Christianity; almost half the population of the world traces its religious background back to this man. He is great, any way you measure him. Well was he named Abraham, "father of a multitude."

We meet him first in the eleventh chapter of Genesis where, in verse 26, we are told that "When Terah had lived seventy years, he became father of Abram." We can fit together some of the pieces of the background of Abraham partly from the facts given us in Scripture, and partly from other facts in history outside the Scriptures. We are told, for instance, in Genesis 11:28, that Haran, one of the sons of Terah and one of the brothers of Abraham, died in the land of his birth—in Ur of the Chaldeans. Now, since the birth of Abram, Nahor, and Haran is reported in a single statement, we can presume that Abraham also was born in Ur. (Many people pronounce that "Er," hence the dictionary so indicates. The modern Arabs of Iraq call it "Or." I think the correct pronunciation should be "Oor.")

However we pronounce it, Ur is not much of a place to look at today. Professor Jack Finegan, in his book *Light from the Ancient Past,* speaks of a disgruntled tourist who wrote in the register of the mud hotel at modern Ur: "No wonder Abraham left; even Job would have!"[1] In a way, you cannot blame the tourist, for Ur is now a barren place away out in the middle of the desert. About all there is to prove that there was once a city on the spot is the remains of a "ziggurat"—an imitation mountain of clay and bitumen, built by people who had come from a mountainous region, to worship their traditional deities. In addition to this ziggurat, we find, in the Iraqi Museum at Baghdad and the Uni-

[1] Jack Finegan, *Light from the Ancient Past* (Princeton: Princeton University Press, 1946), p. 12.

versity Museum at Philadelphia, the rich remains unearthed by archaeologists. From these we are able to reconstruct something of the civilization of Abraham's day.

The approximate date of Abraham's birth we can set at 2000 B.C. The
date is not important. No dates are really important, except that they
are pegs on which we hang our knowledge of the past. We will be able
to hang a few things on this one.

Suppose we try to reconstruct a little of the history of the Mesopotamia that included Ur, just before and after the year 2000 B.C. This
will enable us to fit Abraham into the picture. There is one period of
history known to the historians as the "Old Akkadian" period; they
assign the dates 2360–2180 B.C. The Old Akkadian period had its
pivotal point, its historical and geographical center, in the city of
Akkad—that is where the name "Akkadian" comes from. And the
name of the city of Akkad is usually associated with the name of the
great king, Sargon I. This king is famous, at least, for one thing: he was
the first man in history, so far as we have any record, to claim to be the
ruler of the world. Our modern dictators who have made, or hoped to
make, the same claim—Mussolini, Hitler, Stalin and the rest—are
Johnnies-come-lately, compared to Sargon I. Four thousand years before
they arrived on this earth, Sargon claimed that he had extended his
borders as far as the Upper Sea, the Cedar Forest, and the Silver Mountains. The Upper Sea would be the Mediterranean, the Cedar Forest
would be the Lebanons, and the Silver Mountains would be the Taurus
Mountains in southeastern Asia Minor. Sargon was the first to use the
title, "The King of the Four Quarters of the World."

The Old Akkadian period was one of high level in art. Some day,
I hope you may go into the museum at the University of Pennsylvania
in Philadelphia, or into the Iraqi Museum in the city of Baghdad, and
see some of the magnificent art pieces that have been dug up from the
earth of ancient Mesopotamia.[2] If and when you do, view them with
this fact in mind: many of our teachers, in their enthusiasm to prove
the constant development of art and the human being, select the worst
possible specimens of the past and the best possible of the present, to
show you how it all "progresses" from the poorer to the better. They
may be sincere, but they are wrong, in doing that. Actually, if you
were to pick out the *better* art specimens of the Akkadian period, and

[2] Some beautiful photographs can be found in Leonard Woolley, *Ur: The
First Phases* (London and New York: Penguin Books, 1946).

put them beside some of the monstrosities of "modern art," you would have a very wholesome respect for the Akkadians! Our modern artists take a bit of mud or stone or wood and give it a weird, unrecognizable shape, and call it "Madonna and Child." Looking at this "modern" exhibit, you could prove just the opposite: you could prove that we have degenerated, and not progressed at all.

In the Old Akkadian period, they had writing; they had borrowed it from the Sumerians along with a lot of other things. The Sumerians were a very ancient people; we have no knowledge of the time when they were savages. We meet them first in the fourth millennium b.c. (4000–3000 b.c.), and already they are "a civilized, metal-using people, living in great and populous cities, possessing a complicated system of writing, and living under the government of firmly established civil and religious dynasties and hierarchies."[3] The Sumerians developed the idea of *planned* cities and building, and streets. It is possible also that they developed drainage ditches to get rid of the swamplands in southern Mesopotamia, and probably used them for irrigation purposes as well. They developed the shock tactics of warfare and the phalanx. These did not come into popularity with Caesar; the Sumerians had them two thousand years before the rise of mighty Rome. They also used chariots in war, but not horses, for they had not yet been introduced.[4]

Now all these things belonged to the Sumerians and were handed on by them to the people that followed them in the Old Akkadian period. Then after a brief interlude, the Sumerians came back into power. That would be around the years 2070–1960 b.c. The great name in that period is the name of the king of Lagash, Gudea. You may have heard of him. He laid the foundations for what is known historically as the "Third Dynasty of Ur," and that is the time in which we will have to locate Abraham, so far as I have been able to fit together the facts in the case. This Dynasty wound up by being anti-Semitic; for the Semitic peoples from the Old Akkadian period were so prominent, so popular, so powerful, that the Sumerians felt that they just had to take measures to get rid of them. It has been suggested that this anti-Semitism was the occasion for Abraham's father to take his family out of Ur. It could

[3] H. R. Hall, *The Ancient History of the Near East* (London: Methuen, 1950), 11th ed., p. 172.

[4] A popular, yet scholarly, picture of the Sumerians can be gotten from S. N. Kramer, *From the Tablets of Sumer* (Indian Hills, Colo.: Falcon's Wing Press, 1956), 293 pp.

well be. In the absence of proof, I can only treat this point with a sort of sixth sense. I feel that it would have been the logical time for this separation from the land of Ur.

Following the Sumerian period, we come back into a Semite period called the "Old Babylonian"—which used to be dated around 2000 but which now is dated almost certainly at 1830–1550 B.C. The great name in this period is Hammurabi, the great lawgiver, and one of the first to develop a codified system of law in the ancient world. There were, we now know, other law codes before his.

Where are we going to fit Abraham? In the Old Akkadian period? in the Sumerian period? in the Old Babylonian period? Well, we cannot yet be positive. Scholars used to date Abraham about 2200 B.C. Then when they discovered the records of Hammurabi (who was dated at that time around 2000 B.C.), and because they concluded that the Amraphel of Genesis 14:9 must be Hammurabi, they moved Abraham's dates from 2200 to 2000 B.C. Now that we know Hammurabi lived around the end of the 1800's and the beginning of the 1700's, some scholars have changed Abraham's date again to fit Hammurabi's. Personally, I do not believe we should try to make Abraham and Hammurabi contemporary, for Amraphel and Hammurabi are completely different names, and I see no reason to try to equate them. Moreover, what little we know about Amraphel from Genesis 14 is certainly too little to identify him with the great king of the Babylonians. So if we just forget that and try to fit Abraham into the picture on the basis of other materials, I think we will probably be best satisfied with the Sumerian period just following the time of Gudea, the Third Dynasty of Ur.

We can also work *backwards,* in our Bible chronology, and come out about the same. For example, if we take the date of Solomon, which is reasonably certain, and work back to the time of the Exodus from figures that are given in the Scriptures, and then work back from the time of the Exodus through Joseph and Jacob and Isaac and Abraham, we come out somewhere in the neighborhood of 2000 B.C.

If that is so, and even if we have to give one or two hundred years either way, Abraham fits into the Babylonian civilization at a time when it was at one of its peaks of cultural and political splendor. Now, fifty years ago some critics were telling us that Abraham, "if there were such a person" (and they were not even sure that there had ever been such a person), was a nomad who came out of the desert, with no background of culture, or civilization, who knew nothing about the use of metal, who knew nothing about city life. He was just a vagrant wanderer. Today that can no longer be said. Now we know that Abraham came out of an area which for a long period of time—for four, five or six hundred years—had had a high level of civilization with writing, with fine cities, with highly developed arts, beautiful gems and carvings and very well-established law codes and legal systems; *all* of these things were his, *plus* a highly developed religious system.

According to Joshua 24:2, "Joshua said to all the people, 'Thus says the Lord, the God of Israel, "Your fathers lived of old beyond the Euphrates, Terah, the father of Abraham and of Nahor; and they served other gods." ' " I have found that some people resent the statement that Abraham's father was an idolator. They think that it is heresy to suggest that Abraham came from a line of worshipers of pagan gods. Well, here we have a statement in the Bible itself to the effect that Abraham's father and his brother and probably Abraham himself, at the beginning, were worshipers of false gods. The patron god of the city of Ur was named "Nannar" or "Nanna." (They probably did not pronounce the "r" at the end of a word.) Nanna was the moon god. We know something about the religion of Nanna; we have a lot of records from that period that tell us just how they worshiped, and we know about some of the ritual that they went through to bring honor and glory, as they thought, to the god they served.

It is an interesting fact that Abraham's father, Terah, had a name which in the Hebrew language is related to the word for "moon." It seems likely that his parents—Abraham's grandparents—named this child "Moony" because they were worshipers of Nanna the moon god; only they named him that in Hebrew rather than in Sumerian because they were good Semites.

They doubtless had the old traditions of their people. I think that it is quite likely that these Semitic peoples, who had moved into the area and come in contact with the Sumerians, had brought many stories that had been handed down from generation to generation, probably told around the campfire in front of the tent, from the days when they had lived in the desert. They probably had stories about a flood, and about creation. We know that there were various stories of the flood and various stories of the creation—Babylonian accounts, Sumerian accounts, and a Biblical account, and probably still others.

The details were different, sometimes vastly different. But there is a common denominator in the fact that *there had been a creation* when the world had come into existence by the will of the gods—or God. And there was another common denominator in the fact that there was a time when there had been a flood, and when one family was delivered from it. I suppose Abraham's father had had these traditions. It may well be that the true accounts had been handed down from father to son from the time of Noah and Shem, and that the Hebrew account, which is so different in many details from the Babylonian and Sumerian accounts, had been preserved in the family of Terah, the father of Abraham. We don't know; we are guessing now. But *somebody* must have kept the Biblical account, because it has been preserved for us in our Bible.[5]

Abraham therefore may have had a knowledge of the true God, even though his father was a worshiper of the moon god. Even though he came from a group which had degenerated—let us put it that way— from the worship of the true God to the worship of many false gods, he may still have held on to the tradition that there was a God worshiped by his ancestors who had been the preserver of the human race at the time of the flood of Noah. At any rate, we do know this: one day God called Abraham to get up and get out of that background and to go into another land and build a new civilization. It is sketched for us at the beginning of the twelfth chapter of Genesis: "Now the Lord said to Abram, 'Go from your country and your kindred and your father's house to the land that I will show you. And I will make of you a great nation, and I will bless you, and make your name great.'"

According to Acts 7:2-3, this call came when they were in Mesopotamia. The record is there in Stephen's sermon: "Brethren and fathers, hear me. The God of glory appeared to our father Abraham, when he was in Mesopotamia, before he lived in Haran, and said to him, 'Depart from your land and from your kindred, and go into the land which I will show you.'" When we read the closing verses of the eleventh chapter of Genesis, we get the impression that the call in the first part of the twelfth chapter did not come in Ur, but in Haran. So I think there may have been two calls: an earlier one that was the means whereby God got Abraham out of Ur and as far as Haran; and then the second call whereby God got Abraham "out of the rut"

[5] Unless, of course, we hold that God gave the account *de novo* to Moses. But this, to me, is an unwarranted extension of the doctrine of inspiration.

into which he had settled in Haran, and moved him down into Canaan, where God wanted him in the first place.

There is a fascinating book by a medical doctor named Penfield, entitled *No Other Gods*.[6] It is a novel about Abraham. I was rather interested to read the details in the Preface and the historical notes at the end of the book, and to learn that this book was written by a man who is not a specialist in the field, for it shows a vast amount of research and knowledge of the archaeological discoveries and the historical facts of the period. The doctor has combined these known facts with a wonderful imagination to give us a picture of the life of Abraham in the city of Ur up until the time he finally left it and started on his way to Canaan. The whole novel is written about that one area of his life. The author makes Abraham a priest of Nanna. I do not know whether that was so or not. (The author of historical fiction has at least this advantage over those of us who teach history: he can let his imagination run free once in a while and he can make up little details just so we will have a good story.) Abraham was a priest of Nanna and he became disgusted with paganism and with the ritual that he saw performed: the marriage procession of the god and goddess, the fertility rites, and all the other things that were part and parcel of it. And he felt that certainly, if there is a god who is real, who is worth worshiping, He could not be like this stone idol. The book makes Terah, the father of Abraham, not only a worshiper of false gods but a *maker* of false gods—an idol carver. One day, Terah finished his carving and said, "There, I have made you!" Abraham noticed that, and he thought about it. What kind of god is this that is only a piece of stone or wood until man gets finished and says, "There, I have made you; now you're a god"?

All this leads directly, in our novel, to the initial call of Abraham by the true God. Here is a young man with good training, and a good background, who comes to realize that this idol manufacture and worship is not true, and cannot be real. Thinking his way through, he comes later to an experience of the real God; he is "called out" by that God. Somewhere, some time, in Ur of the Chaldeans, there came a call from God to Abraham to get up and leave that place. Perhaps it was connected with the anti-Semitic movement among the Sumerians of the Third Dynasty of Ur, during which this family was expelled

[6] Wilder Penfield, *No Other Gods* (Boston: Little, Brown and Co., 1954), 341 pp.

from the city. Whatever the circumstances, they returned to the country from which their ancestors had come a generation or two before: Haran which is in Padan-Aram, up in the great bend of the River Euphrates, just south of the Armenian highland, a little east of what we know today as Asia Minor. In that region they settled down and Abraham stayed there until his father died, and perhaps a little longer. Life was so good and easy there that he seemed to forget that God had called him. So God called the second time, telling Abraham to get out of Haran and go to Canaan, where he would be safely away from the worship of the moon god, where he would have an opportunity to pioneer in the development of a nation which will know the one true God, and follow Him. "Go from your country and your kindred and your father's house to the land that I will show you. And I will make of you a great nation, and I will bless you, and make your name great." Ultimately, that blessing is to reach all men.

Here is the central thought, in this first study of Abraham: *the Hebrew faith and the Christian religion begin with a call from God.* That is a basic fact from which we cannot escape. We have no right to try to escape from it. As I understand the Scripture record, I do not see here an account of mere human curiosity. I cannot believe that simply because this young man of Semitic background became disgusted with the ways and worship of the anti-Semitic people among whom he lived he was "led to invent something better," as some have put it. I cannot believe that his religion was a product of the human mind alone. There was something beyond all that. It is the clear-cut teaching of Genesis, and of all the rest of the Bible, *that the initial move came from God, and not from Abraham.* If God had not called, he might have stayed in Ur or Haran and worshiped the moon god until he died. It was necessary that God take the initiative, that God come to him and say, "There is something better for you than what you have in this pagan world."

There was a lot of sacrifice involved, as we shall see in our next chapter on the faith of Abraham. He was leaving a well-established civilization to go out into a country that was rather backward—as he probably knew, for there had been commerce with Canaan and military expeditions to Canaan before Abraham's time in the days of King Sargon I. It was not so well civilized as Egypt or Babylon; yet Abraham was willing to give up all of his comfort and his advantages. If he were to have any children in the years to come—he did not have at that time, because "Sarah was barren"—he would have to bring them up where there were no schools and few if any of the advantages that they would have had in Ur. But God called him, and he was obedient to that call.

This is the way God deals with each one of us. He may not wait for our curiosity to get the best of us. He may not wait for us to reach the place where we are disgusted with the ways of the world.

Sometimes we are called to weigh the disadvantages of giving up the background that we have, the culture that we enjoy. It may be a question very much like the one Abraham had to face; where will our children grow up if we follow the call of God? But God calls, and He expects us to hear that call and to obey it. The man who obeys is a man of faith; the man who disobeys is a man without faith, an unbeliever. It was possible for Abraham to have a great name and become a great nation and a source of blessing to all the world only if by hearing and obeying the call of God. So it ever is for Abraham's seed.

CHAPTER II

Abraham: The Response

IN THE ELEVENTH chapter of the Epistle to the Hebrews—what someone has called "The Westminster Abbey of the Bible"—there is a roll call of the great heroes of the Hebrew faith. In this roll call, Abraham is mentioned three times. By faith Abraham heard the call of God and obeyed; by faith he sojourned in the land of Canaan; by faith he offered up his son Isaac (Hebrews 11:8, 9, 17).

We considered Abraham's call in the last chapter. It took faith to answer that call, and Abraham had faith; he "went out, not knowing where he was to go." He left Ur and Haran, which were in the land of Mesopotamia (we call it Iraq today), for Canaan. What were his thoughts? What did he know about Canaan?

Mesopotamia was in a period of a high degree of culture and well-developed civilization when Abraham shook its dust from his feet. So was Egypt. And the land of Canaan lay between Mesopotamia and Egypt. There was constant communication between these two great lands, as we know from the very detailed records now available.

Now the traveler from Egypt to Mesopotamia had to pass through the land of Canaan. We read in the records of one Egyptian traveler, an exile from the court of Pharaoh Sesotris I (1980–1936 B.C., which was about the time of Abraham), who passed through the land of milk and honey and left this written record about it: "Here are figs and grapes more wine than water; honey is plentiful, oil is all abundant; all kinds of fruit hang upon the trees. Barley and wheat grow in the fields, and there are countless herds of all types."[1] He went on to rejoice in the fact that his native language, Egyptian, was spoken in the Canaanite villages he visited. What he tells of the land was probably true of a part of the land, rather than of all of it. It was a delightful country, but still a backward country; it did not know the high level of civilization found in Egypt or Mesopotamia.

[1] The Story of Sinuhe in *Ancient Near Eastern Texts Relating to the Old Testament*, J. B. Pritchard, ed. (Princeton: Princeton University Press, 1955), 2nd ed., p. 19.

In the introduction of a fine atlas on Bible lands,[2] the editors point out a peculiar paradox about the land of Palestine. It was a land in association with the rest of the world of its day; it was the land bridge connecting the world of that day, namely: Asia Minor and the Hittite empire, Mesopotamia and the Babylonian and Sumerian civilizations, and Egypt. To get from one to the other, you had to go through Canaan, for Canaan lay at the heart of them. Literally, if you were to take a map of this world and draw an "X" across it, the crossing of the "X" would lie over Canaan, and the arms would stretch into Asia Minor and Babylonia and Egypt and the Arabian Peninsula. Canaan was the crossroads of the world—and yet, as these editors point out, it stood in *contrast* with the rest of world, in what they call "a splendid isolation." By and large the country was mountainous and not given to a network of highways. (There were two highways: one went along the coast, the other via the borderland of the Transjordanian Plateau, along the edge of the desert.) Canaan was separated from the rest of the world on the west by the sea, on the east by the desert, on the south by the desert, and on the north by mountains. So the people of Canaan, though on the trade routes connecting the rest of the world, were after all isolated by sea, desert, and mountain. They lived pretty much to themselves, and therefore their civilization was retarded, compared to the greater lands and peoples who surrounded them.

This is why, I believe, God wanted Abraham and his people in Canaan. Because, you see, when you are part of an ambitious nation in the midst of the confusion of the world, you have less chance of hearing God speak than when you are more isolated. The people of Canaan could keep up with what was going on in the world, if they wanted to. All they had to do was to ask the men in the caravans that passed through Canaan, "What's happening in Egypt? What's new in Mesopotamia?" They could keep up with the news, and yet be far enough removed from the hubbub of life to meditate, and listen for the voice of God.

Abraham was called to go and settle in this land. It took *faith,* as we have already said, for him to obey that call. The author of Hebrews tells us that "By faith Abraham obeyed. . . . By faith he sojourned in the land of promise. . . . For he looked forward to the city which has foundations, whose builder and maker is God" (Hebrews 11:8-10).

[2] *The Westminster Historical Atlas to the Bible,* G. E. Wright and F. V. Filson, eds. (Philadelphia: Westminster Press, 1956), 2nd ed., 130 pp.

It is a noteworthy fact of history that Ur perished. It fell into ruins, and the wind-driven dust of the desert buried it deep. We did not even know where it was until Sir Leonard Woolley and his archaeological expedition turned up its ruins in the 1920's and 1930's. That splendid city, capital of the magnificent Third Dynasty of Ur, was completely lost to history for nearly three thousand years. History records the same fate for Egypt. The great capital Memphis, for example—the "Noph" of the Old Testament, or "Moph," as it is sometimes called—is today little more than a few fallen statues covered with sand and weeds. But with the city whose builder and maker is God it is vastly different!

Jerusalem, to me, is a parable of this truth, for the Holy City has stood there all through the centuries; there Jerusalem shall always stand. The civilizations of Egypt and Mesopotamia have collapsed, but the faith of Abraham has endured, and been handed on down to us. Abraham had faith to believe that when God called him to leave Ur for Canaan, God meant business, and Abraham was ready to go into business with God. For this reason the Jew speaks reverently of "our father, Abraham"; for this reason the Arab calls him "the friend of God"; and for this reason the Christian looks upon him as the father of the Household of Faith (Galatians 3:7).

Abraham had a promise from God, as well as a call. The promise was that he would have a seed. We read in the twelfth chapter of Genesis: "I will make of you a great nation." And we find it mentioned again in the fifteenth chapter: "After these things the word of the Lord came to Abram in a vision, 'Fear not, Abram, I am your shield; your reward shall be very great.' But Abram said, 'O Lord God, what wilt thou give me, for I continue childless, and the heir of my house is Eliezer of Damascus?' [Eliezer was his slave.] And Abram said, 'Behold, thou hast given me no offspring; and a slave born in my house shall be my heir'" (15:1-3). That may seem strange to us, but it was the custom of the day. We know, thanks to the discovery of certain ancient clay tablets that have been dug up in Mesopotamia, that when a man was childless, a slave born in his house inherited his estate.[3] But the Lord said, "This man shall not be your heir; your own son shall be your heir. And he brought him outside and said, 'Look toward

[3] For this and other customs of the day, see E. Chiera, *They Wrote on Clay* (Chicago: University of Chicago Press, 1938), 233 pp. A paperback edition (Phoenix Books) was published in 1957. See also C. H. Gordon, *The Living Past* (New York: John Day Co., 1941), pp. 156-178.

heaven, and number the stars, if you are able to number them. . . . So shall your descendants be.' And he believed the Lord; and he reckoned it to him as righteousness" (15:4-6).

Abraham, we are led to believe, had faith in that promise of God, faith that God would fulfill it, and raise up from his "seed" a great multitude. Or—did he? Suppose we study it, closely.

Go back to Genesis 12 and read: "Now there was a famine in the land [that is, of course, after they reached Canaan]. So Abraham went down to Egypt to sojourn there, for the famine was severe in the land. And when he was about to enter Egypt he said to Sarai his wife, 'I know you are a woman beautiful to behold; when the Egyptians see you they will say, "This is his wife"; then they will kill me and let you live. Say you are my sister, that it may go well with me because of you, and that my life may be spared on your account' " (12:10-13).

Just think of the possibilities in all this! It was, of course, not a *complete* lie; we know that Sarai was Abraham's half-sister. But by presenting Sarai as his sister Abraham was putting God's promise into jeopardy. For if one of the Egyptians were to look upon her and fall in love with her and take her to be his wife, and if Sarai should bear a child to that Egyptian, the promise of God would come to nought. It may come to us as a surprise that God used the pagan Pharaoh to frustrate that plan.

At that particular time, Egypt had reached one of the high peaks of her history. The history of Egypt could be represented by a curved line with three or four peaks or elevations along the line; the main periods that we call the "Old Kingdom" and the "Middle Kingdom" are two of the highest peaks.[4] Like Mesopotamia, Egypt had had a history that stretched far back into antiquity. Four thousand years before Christ the Egyptians were already refining copper and making pottery; they had boats on the Nile; they lived in villages. Three thousand years before Christ they had invented a system of writing which continued to be used right on down into Christian times. The hieroglyphs on the tombs and monuments and stelae of Egypt had been invented more than a thousand years before Abraham's day.

The Great Pyramids had been built in the Old Kingdom period (2700-2200 B.C.). The greatest of the pyramids built by Cheops in the Fourth Dynasty, the "Great Pyramid of Gizeh," contains 2,300,000

---

[4] See G. Steindorff and K. C. Seele, *When Egypt Ruled the East* (Chicago: University of Chicago Press, 1942), 284 pp.

blocks of granite, each one of them weighing several tons. The height of the pyramid was 481 feet; its sides were 755 feet long, and according to one of the scholars who has made a comprehensive study of the pyramids,[5] the precision with which these blocks were cut and worked into shape was so accurate that when the blocks were laid up it was not necessary to put mortar between the courses—they fit precisely. The pyramid is as close to square as it is possible for any structure to be square. Modern engineering methods could not improve upon the shape and the tooling of those stones. "Precision, organized labor, planning, varied personnel (from drudges to masons and up to the master architect), and the backing of the entire economy were necessary" to establish the greatest of the seven wonders of the ancient world, says Cyrus Gordon, and he reminds us that of all of the seven wonders of the ancient world, it is the only one that exists down to the present time.[6]

This pyramid was already seven hundred years old when Abraham and his people were there, the time when Abraham lost his faith temporarily and said, "Don't say you are my wife; tell them you are my sister." And it took an Egyptian Pharaoh to remind Abraham of the moral question involved. Pharaoh called Abraham (12:18-19) and said, "What is this you have done to me? Why did you not tell me that she was your wife? Why did you say, 'She is my sister,' so that I took her for my wife? Now then, here is your wife, take her, and be gone." And he sent Abraham away.

The faith of Abraham and his wife Sarah is portrayed for us again in the story of Sarah and her handmaid, Hagar. Read the opening verses (Genesis 16:1-2): "Now Sarai, Abram's wife, bore him no children. She had an Egyptian maid whose name was Hagar; and Sarai said to Abram, 'Behold now, the Lord has prevented me from bearing children; go in to my maid; it may be that I shall obtain children by her.'"

That, too, was the custom of the time. I know that the morals involved in this offend many Christians of the twentieth century A.D., but Abraham and Sarah were not living in the twentieth century A.D. They had never heard the words of Jesus Christ. They had never read the

---

[5] I. E. S. Edwards, *The Pyramids of Egypt* ("Pelican Books"; Baltimore: Penguin Books, 1947), 256 pp.

[6] C. H. Gordon, *Introduction to Old Testament Times* (Ventnor, N. J.: Ventnor Publishers, 1953), p. 48.

Ten Commandments of Moses. They lived before those things. And they were following the custom of their day. We have marriage contracts which were dug up at Nuzu (near modern Kirkuk, Iraq), in which the details of the marriage are set down and agreed to and signed by each of the parties contracting, signed by the witnesses, and their seals rolled across the face of the tablet, to make it a marriage contract; in these contracts the woman promises to give her husband children. It is stated in some of the contracts, where the details are given more fully, that if she cannot produce children herself, she shall provide them through her handmaid.[7] Now, she signed a *contract* to do that; and I have no doubt that Sarah had agreed to a similar contract with Abraham, and was fulfilling the contract. She had no children. So she was to have a child, Ishmael, through Hagar. Of course this was lack of faith on the part both of Abraham and Sarah. We can excuse the morality of it, when we consider the customs of the day, but we cannot blame their lack of faith on the customs of the day.

In Genesis 17:15-17 we read: "And God said to Abraham, 'As for Sarai your wife, you shall not call her name Sarai, but Sarah shall be her name. I will bless her, and moreover I will give you a son by her; I will bless her, and she shall be a mother of nations; kings of people shall come from her.' Then Abraham fell on his face and laughed, and said to himself, 'Shall a child be born to a man who is a hundred years old? Shall Sarah, who is ninety years old, bear a child?'" In the eighteenth chapter, Sarah was told by the messengers of God that she was to bear a child and, remembering her age, she burst into laughter. God said to Abraham, "Why did Sarah laugh?" Sarah denied it, but God was not mocked: "But you *did* laugh!" Neither of them, you see, had the faith to believe that God could give them a child so late in life.

As we go on and read of the casting out of Hagar, after the child Ishmael was born, after Sarah had conceived in her old age and given birth to Isaac, we see another sign of lack of faith. It was all clearly covered by the laws of the time. Legally, Sarah had the right to send Hagar away; for Hagar was Sarah's property. Abraham admitted that. But the law of the day also said specifically that if the man's wife is unable to conceive, and if her handmaid does, and produces a child for the family, and then, later, the legal wife has a son of her own, the son of her handmaid takes second place. If Hagar had stayed there

[7] See C. H. Gordon, "Biblical Customs and the Nuzu Tablets," *The Biblical Archaeologist,* 3 (1940), pp. 2-3.

with Ishmael, there was no question at all about the lineage or inheritance according to the laws of the day: Ishmael would have been second to Isaac. There was no need to drive out Hagar. There was no need to drive out Ishmael. It was simply lack of faith, on the part of Abraham and Sarah.

I mention these things because I want you to see, when we are talking about a man who stands as *the* man of faith in all of history, that his faith may not always have been 100 per cent. Some of you, at times, will be discouraged because your faith is so weak. Take heart! Even Abraham, the father of all the faithful, was a man whose faith was not always quite strong enough.

In addition to numerous descendants, Abraham was also promised a land, the land of Canaan. We read in Genesis 15:13-15, "Then the Lord said to Abraham, 'Know of a surety that your descendants will be sojourners in a land that is not theirs, and will be slaves there, and they will be oppressed for four hundred years; but I will bring judgment on the nation which they serve, and afterward they shall come out with great possessions. As for yourself, you shall go to your fathers in peace; you shall be buried in good old age. And they shall come back here in the fourth generation.'" God draws the boundaries of the land in the eighteenth verse: ". . . from the river of Egypt to the great river, the river Euphrates." The river of Egypt mentioned here is not the Nile, but the little seasonal river (or wadi) in the desert south of the land of Canaan, quite a bit north of the Nile. Its modern name is Wadi el-'Arish. God determined where this land was to be, and that it was to belong to Abraham and his descendants. But—think of it!—Abraham was not to live long enough to enjoy it. He would die there. But his sons and grandsons and great grandsons would be exiled, driven out of it. It would not be theirs until the fourth generation.

Abraham actually dwelled in the new land for about a hundred years, and at the end of that time, how much of Canaan do you think he owned? Only a little burial plot he had bought of the Hittites, where he could lay Sarah's bones to rest! That was all he had. He *lived* there, but he never *owned* the land. If ever you have questioned his faith, your questions should be answered as you watch him in this experience, recorded in the twenty-third chapter.

Sarah died at Kiriath-arba in the land of Canaan; we know it better as Hebron. Grieving and heartbroken, Abraham turned to the Hittites and said to them, "I am a stranger and a sojourner among you.

Give me property among you, for a burying place." Then in true Oriental manner, they bargained: "Oh, we couldn't sell it to *you*! Just go ahead and take it." And Abraham replied, in effect, "Oh, no, gentlemen; I couldn't take it that way. How much do you want for it?" "Well, it's worth $250—but what is that among friends? Take it and bury your dead." So Abraham paid the amount suggested. According to the seventeenth verse, "the field with the cave in it, the field of Ephron and Machpelah, which was to the east of Mamre, the field with the cave which was in it and all the trees that were in the field, throughout its whole area, was made over to Abraham as a possession in the presence of the Hittites, before all who went in at the gate of his city." So he buried his wife there, in what had become his possession. It was Abraham's way of taking a pledge for four hundred years; four hundred years later his great grandchildren would come back and take over this land, and it would be theirs.

Now we come to the really great test of his faith, in Genesis 22, where God tells him to take his son—the son that he didn't have enough faith to believe he was going to have, and that Sarah didn't have enough faith to believe that she would be able to bear—he was to take this child Isaac "up unto the Mount of Moriah" (which is at the present time under the temple area in the city of Jerusalem) and offer him as a burnt offering. Genesis 22:2 says, "Take your son, your only son Isaac, whom you love. . . ." I think each phrase that God spoke to Abraham, must have stabbed another knife into his heart. "Take your son . . . your only son . . . Isaac . . . the one that you love . . . and offer him there as a burnt offering. . . ." By this time Abraham had become a man of tremendous faith. He was a man of faith before, but his faith was weak at times. This time it is great.

Try to understand what is involved. God had promised Abraham that his seed, his posterity, would be the hope of the whole world—not his slave Eliezer, not the son of his handmaid Hagar, Ishmael, but the son of Sarah would be the one who would fulfill that promise. Now God asked him to sacrifice the boy! It would have been hard enough to offer up Eliezer, who had worked for him all of those years; it would have been hard enough to offer up Ishmael, because he loved the lad and wept when he was sent away. It would have been hard enough if God had come and asked Abraham to offer his own life as a sacrifice. But, if he had offered his own life, there would still have been Isaac to carry out the promise. But God did not ask that. God put

His finger on the only person through whom the promise could be fulfilled, and said, "Offer *him* up."

If Isaac were killed, all of the promises that had been made to Abraham would become of no value. Yet Abraham was willing to go through with it. And the writer of the Epistle to the Hebrews gives us some suggestion of why. Some men say, "Abraham had faith to believe that God would not ask him to go all the way through with it; he had the feeling that God would take him up there on the mountain and then would back down and give him a second choice." *That* is not faith! The writer of Hebrews tells us that Abraham was so sure that God would be able to raise up that child *from the dead*, if necessary, that he was willing to go through and offer him up. *That* is faith!

In a way, you and I stand in the same relation to the world as Abraham did. There is a sense in which our children and our children's children have their faith because we keep ours. And the world that still needs the salvation which God provides can only hope for that salvation through those of us who have that faith. Abraham was imperfect and his faith was weak, but at the end, when he came to the last great test, he came through triumphant. You and I are expected to have that same faith that takes God at His word, faith that believes God means it when He tells us that He is going to save this world through His own Son.

I can never think about the willingness of Abraham to offer up his son Isaac without thinking of the willingness of God to offer up His Son Jesus. God provided a lamb to take the place of Isaac, but there was no lamb to take the place of Jesus. *He was the Lamb!* You and I have our life and our salvation and our hope of eternity because of what God has done for us in Christ; and the only way this world will ever come to know the salvation that we know will be by way of our faithfulness. God expects us to be faithful.

CHAPTER III

Jacob

THE THIRTY-SECOND chapter of Genesis contains the story of one of the most famous wrestling-bouts in all history. It is worth repeating.

The same night he arose and took his two wives, his two maids, and his eleven children, and crossed the ford of the Jabbok. He took them and sent them across the stream, and likewise everything that he had. And Jacob was left alone; and a man wrestled with him until the breaking of the day. When the man saw that he did not prevail against Jacob, he touched the hollow of his thigh; and Jacob's thigh was put out of joint as he wrestled with him. Then he said, "Let me go, for the day is breaking." But Jacob said, "I will not let you go, unless you bless me." And he said to him, "What is your name?" And he said, "Jacob." Then he said, "Your name shall no more be called Jacob, but Israel, for you have striven with God and with men, and have prevailed." Then Jacob said, "Tell me, I pray you, your name." But he said, "Why is it that you ask my name?" And there he blessed him. So Jacob called the name of the place Peniel, saying, "For I have seen God face to face, and yet my life is preserved." (Genesis 32:22-30)

This is Jacob, son of Isaac, grandson of the mighty Abraham. His life may be presented as a drama in three acts. The first act deals with the men he knew, and loved or despised; and the first of these men is Isaac. Isaac is hardly worth a chapter of his own in this book: he committed the sins of his father Abraham, he made no advances on the faith of that father, and he was, all in all, a rather colorless personality. And yet, in Hebrews 11:20, we read that "by faith Isaac invoked future blessings on Jacob and Esau"—and that makes him important.

If Isaac had lived in the Christian dispensation, we might call him a "second generation Christian"—that is, one who grew up knowing Christ not from his own experience but through parents who knew Him. Isaac was typical of that kind of religion. It is true, in the light of the total picture, that he did have some appreciation of spiritual values. Many Christians, you know, fail to find in the Christianity which they get from their parents a source of power for their own lives.

31

Isaac was not quite as bad as that. With all his weaknesses, with all his lack of color, in spite of the fact that "this world was too much with him," he still blessed Jacob and Esau and passed on to them the great spiritual blessings that were his.

Jacob was his mother Rebekah's favorite; Esau was the favorite of his father. There are several scenes proving that. You will remember that Isaac was getting along in life, and that in his old age, thinking he was near the end, he asked for a dish of venison stew. Esau, the hunter, the man of the fields could provide that; if he would bring it, Isaac said, he would give his son the parental blessing. Off goes Esau— and in comes Rebekah!

They lived in tents, in those days, and it was not hard for Rebekah to "listen in" from the other side of the goat-hair cloth, or from another part of the tent. She heard it, and she rushed to Jacob. We can almost hear her saying, "Get busy now, son, *quickly*. We'll get that blessing for you!" Jacob liked the idea—but there was one hitch. Jacob had been born with a smooth, soft skin, while his brother Esau had rough, hair-covered skin; when the blind father touched him in giving the blessing, he would know immediately that he was touching Jacob, and not Esau. "Perhaps my father will feel me," suggests Jacob, "and I shall seem to be mocking him, and bring a curse upon myself and not a blessing." That did not stop Rebekah; she covered the backs of his hands and neck with a rough goat's skin, so that when the old man touched it, he would think he was touching Esau. It was a deception that seems incredible on the part of any mother and wife.

You can lay part of the blame on Rebekah, but the larger part of the deception was Jacob's. When the father asks, "Who are you, my son?" Jacob replies, "I am Esau, your first-born. I have done as you told me; now sit up and eat of my game, that you may bless me." Isaac is suspicious: "How is it that you have found it so quickly?" Then Jacob adds blasphemy to lie: "Because the Lord your God granted me success." Still uncertain, blind Isaac would touch his son: "Come near, that I may feel you, my son. . . ." He will know the difference, thanks to his well-developed sense of touch, between smooth-skinned Jacob and rough-skinned Esau. And he touches the goat-skin, and says, pitifully, "The voice is Jacob's voice, but the hands are the hands of Esau!" He asks the question a third time: "Are you *really* my son Esau?" And again the lie: "I am."

It is an awesome picture of deception—and the guilt lies upon all three: on Jacob, for it was he who gave the direct lie; on Rebekah, for it was she who planned the lie; and upon Isaac, the overfond parent whose favoritism toward one of his sons sowed the seeds of dissension which were to wreak such havoc later in the family.

Esau, as the second man in Jacob's life, is worth careful consideration. When Jacob was born, according to the story in Genesis 25, he was born as the twin of Esau. Esau was the first-born. There was a struggle between the two in the womb of the mother and Jacob was delivered holding on to the heel of Isaac, so he was named "Jacob," "a supplanter"—one who sought to take the place of his brother.

Now, of course, we know that at such an early age there could have been no decision of self-expression in the minds or wills of the children being born. Paul holds, in his argument in Romans, that this was a case of divine sovereignty and election, and not at all the choice of the child. Nevertheless, a bitterness developed between the two which ripened, in later life, into hatred. For instance, read the story of the selling of the birthright, in Genesis 25:29-34. Esau comes in from his hunting famished and finds Jacob boiling pottage. He begs for some of it. Jacob is willing to share the meal with his hungry brother, but, "First, sell me your birthright!" Esau, stabbed with pangs of hunger, says, "I am about to die; of what use is a birthright to me?" So he sells it to his brother Jacob for a mess of pottage! It sounds strange to us, especially when we know more about what that birthright was. It was the precious right of primogeniture: the first-born son had the right to take his father's place upon the father's death and become the head, the ruling member of the family.

We know from the Nuzu tablets that were discovered near Kirkuk in 1926, that one of the important elements of life in that day was the birthright, which could be bought and sold. For example, Kurpazah, the son of Hilbishuh, obtained a grove belonging to his brother Tupkitilla in exchange for three sheep.[1] Apparently Tupkitilla, too, was hungry; he wanted something to eat so badly that he was willing to sell his birthright to get it: he gave away his right to his father's fruitful orchard for a mouthful to eat!

Perhaps there is another side to this story that seems so hard to understand. It is possible that some men held the birthright so cheaply because they did not want the headache that went with it, for the birthright was not only a privilege but a responsibility. You see, from the

[1] See C. H. Gordon, *The Living Past*, p. 177.

time he became the elder in the family, the holder of the birthright had to make all decisions for the family. It was in my lifetime and yours too, that a man gave up the crown of the British Empire for the woman he loved; and many of us felt that it may have been not just for the woman he loved, but also for the desire to escape the responsibility, the burden of being tied down to the cares of the Empire. Esau was simply not interested in his birthright and what it implied—the religious heritage as well as the cultural heritage of Isaac. Esau was of the earth, earthy, a worldly man; he had no sense of values. That is illustrated again, I think, by the fact that he was so careless of his father's will that he went out and married two Hittite women, even though it was the expressed desire of the patriarch that the wives of these men should not be Canaanites or Hittites, but of the same stock as the patriarchs themselves, namely Hebrew women. Esau's whole life was a renunciation of the values of Abraham and Isaac. He just did not care about those things.

The third significant man in Jacob's life is Laban, his uncle. You remember the story of how, after the hatred between Esau and Jacob had developed to the place where it was no longer safe for Jacob to stay home, his mother sent him away, and he went to live with his Uncle Laban, his mother's brother; and of how he met Rachel and fell in love with her. He worked seven years and then another seven for her.

Now I have no certain knowledge from the Scripture itself, but I think, judging from the customs of the times, that we have here what is known as a marriage adoption. No sons of Laban are mentioned at this time; they are mentioned later. According to the custom of the day, a man who had no sons of his own to look after him in his old age, and to take over the right of primogeniture and carry on the family and the family tradition, could marry his daughter to a young man under a marriage adoption contract, in which, in exchange for giving his daughter to this young man, he took the young man as his son and conferred upon him the rights of sonship. It is further stated in those marriage documents that should a son, a *true* son, be born to the man later, that son would take the place of primogeniture and the son-in-law (the adopted son) would lose it. I think that is what must have happened in the case of Jacob with Laban, because later on we come across a reference to Laban's sons, and Laban is sending Jacob off without the rights, or the title. Jacob would have lost it entirely except for the fact that Rachel stole the teraphim, originally the images of the family gods,[2] possession of which we know now was guarantee to the title. The person who held the teraphim was the person who could prove thereby that he had claim to all of the property of the father. When Rachel stole the teraphim, it was not because she was worshiping them, but because she knew that if she did not hold on to them, her husband Jacob would never have any legal claim on Laban's estate.[3]

Well, Laban was a hard man to work for. We read in the story that after Jacob had served his seven years he woke up the morning after the wedding to find that he had been given the less desirable Leah, Rachel's older sister, instead of his beloved Rachel. Of course he objected; but Laban told him, "It is not so done in our country to give the younger before the first-born. Complete the week of this one and we will give you the other also—in return for serving me another seven years" (29:26). Jacob—and how we admire him for it!—accepted the bargain; he married Rachel at the end of the week, and he worked seven more long years to keep her. And six years beyond that.

His wages were to be a part of Laban's flocks; he was to have every speckled and spotted sheep and every black lamb, and every spotted and speckled goat. Jacob worked on, in good faith, only to be double-crossed by the crafty uncle again: the very day of the agreement, Laban cut out of his flocks every speckled and spotted lamb, sheep, and goat, and hid them from Jacob, putting a distance of three days' journey between himself and Jacob! It was a detestable trick—but this time Jacob won: read Genesis 30:37-43 to see how he did it. It was one man of guile against another, but in the end, Jacob comes off the better man. Jacob sums up his experience with Laban in Genesis 31:41-42: "These twenty years I have been in your house; I have served you fourteen years for your two daughters, and six years for your flock, and you have changed my wages ten times. If the God of my father, the God of

[2] The word *teraphim* is a Hebrew plural. If this strikes the reader as polytheism or idolatry, let us remember that there was, until the Exile, a constant struggle between the purer form of Jehovah-worship and the idolatry and polytheism of the common people. If this had not been so, there would have been no reason for the command, "Thou shalt have no other gods . . ." and no reason for the preaching of the prophets. Nor would the words of Genesis 35:2 to Jacob have been necessary, "Put away the foreign gods that are among you."

[3] A different view is given in P. Heinisch, *History of the Old Testament*, W. Heidt, trans. (Collegeville, Minn.: Liturgical Press, 1952), p. 58. This Roman Catholic author suggests that Rachel wanted to be able to invoke the gods' protection and deprive Laban of their power. Where Scripture is silent, the Bible student must be content with *probable* explanations.

Abraham, and the Fear of Isaac had not been on my side, surely now you would have sent me away empty-handed. God saw my affliction and the labor of my hands, and rebuked you. . . ."

That was Laban, and that was Jacob. We can sum it up by studying the response of Jacob to the people around him. He was a man of deception; he had learned that from his mother. He *had* to deceive to get along with his father, to get along with his brother, to get along with his crafty uncle. At least, he thought he did. He was the first one of a long line to follow the principle that "the end justifies the means." Do evil that good may come!

Now look at Jacob and the women in his life. There was, of course, his mother, Rebekah, a strong character but a sly one. We have already mentioned her deception of her husband Isaac. When Jacob suggested that they might get caught, and that he would receive a curse instead of a blessing, she said, "Upon me be your curse, my son; only obey my word and go. . . ." Well, for her deception she lost her son. She was forced to send him away and she never saw him again. When he returned, she was dead.

His wife Rachel is the second important woman in his life, and with her we see Jacob in a different light. Here we have one of those facets of character that show up to tell us that Jacob is not all bad. We learn that he was a strong man. We had not known about that side of his nature until we read about how he came near to the house of Laban and saw the shepherds around the well. There was a large stone on the mouth of the well, so large that no one shepherd was able to move it. But when Jacob saw Rachel, he walked over and moved the stone all by himself. He was a big burly man, and he was going to show this beautiful young girl that he was the kind of man that she ought to marry. Then he fell in love with her. He must have really fallen in love, because he used none of his guile or craft to get her. We read in 29:20 the simple statement that Jacob "served seven years for Rachel, and they seemed to him but a few days because of the love he had for her." We see a different side of the man there. There is a tenderness of character, a depth of devotion, a real sense of value when it comes to the one truly-loved woman in his life.

There were others, of course. There were the Hittite sisters-in-law, the women whom Esau married, who gave him so much trouble. There was his daughter Dinah who was ravished by one of the men of the neighborhood, who later, but for the objections of her brothers, would have married her: the affair ended in a massacre. But Jacob was no ruthless murderer as were his sons. His response, especially in the area of the women of his life, was one of sorrow and suffering and separation.

Last of all, we come to study the relations between Jacob and his God. There are four episodes, or four scenes, here. Scene 1: Bethel. Jacob falls asleep and dreams a dream in which he sees a ladder from heaven to earth, with angels going up and coming down. God comes to him (Genesis 28:13) and repeats the promise He had made to Abraham: "I am the Lord, the God of Abraham your father, and the God of Isaac; the land on which you lie I will give to you and to your descendants; and your descendants shall be like the dust of the earth, and you shall spread abroad to the west and to the east and to the north and to the south; and by you and your descendants shall all the families of the earth bless themselves. Behold, I am with you and will keep you wherever you go, and will bring you back to this land; for I will not leave you until I have done that of which I have spoken to you" (28:13-15). It was the promise that God would always be with Jacob, that the God of his fathers was *his* God.

Scene 2: Jabbok. (Read Genesis 32:22-32.) Jacob wrestles with the angel of the Lord. Here his name is changed to Israel; it is actually the great moment of change for his whole life. All the deception and guile, all the lies and blasphemous pretense, seem to go out of his life with this event. He becomes a mellow man, touched not only in the thigh by the angel of the Lord, but in the heart by the Lord Himself. Throughout the rest of his life we find him a moderating influence trying to hold those unruly sons of his together, protesting when they rise up in the affair of Dinah, telling them, "You have brought trouble on me by making me odious to the inhabitants of the land ..." (34:30). They had. And *he* had, in the past. But the past was past. It was over and done. This is a new Jacob now. He has broken with the people and the gods of his yesterdays. He calls his family together (35:9) and tells them to put away their foreign gods and idols, the gods and idols they had brought out of Padan-Aram. He is quits with these things. He is God's man now.

Scene 3: The second episode at Bethel. In chapter 35, God renews the Bethel episode, because as I see it, between the first Bethel and the second, Jacob had moved out of the country to Mesopotamia, to Padan-Aram, and now he had come back into the land. We have here one of the clear-cut indications of Scripture that God's promise to Israel is directly associated with the land of Israel. While Jacob was in that land, God promised to bless him. When he had moved out of the land, apparently no blessing followed except through providential oversight. But when he comes back, God renews the promise and tells him that He will be with him, and that Jacob will be a means whereby the people of the world are to be blessed. God renews the statement, "Your name is . . . no longer Jacob, but Israel . . ."; and renews the promise, ". . . the land which I gave to Abraham and Isaac I will give to you, and I will give the land to your descendants after you" (35:9). I personally do not believe that the promises made to Israel can have any final fulfillment except in the land of Israel. I believe that God has tied down His promises to Israel to that particular spot of the earth, and I believe that He will keep His word and bless that region for His Name's sake.

Scene 4: Just before Jacob goes into Egypt, when he is down at Beersheba at the southern end of the land. God comes to him and says, "I am God, the God of your father; do not be afraid to go down to Egypt; for I will there make of you a great nation. I will go down with you to Egypt and I will also bring you up again; and Joseph's hand shall close your eyes" (46:1-4). That was a remarkable revelation! Up until this time His people seem to have the idea that as long as they stay in Canaan, God will be there, but when they move out of Canaan, God will not go with them. But now God says clearly, "You are going to Egypt. You are going with my permission. I am going with you." And they begin to get a bigger view of God and a better understanding of His will.

The name of Jacob appears many times in the Bible; I have read somewhere that it appears more often than any other name except the names of God. And it is interesting that God regularly calls Himself "the God of Jacob." And when the Scripture refers to "the God of Israel," it does not refer to Jacob as a person, but to Israel as a people, as the descendants of Jacob; but when God refers to a person, He calls Himself the God of Jacob: "I am the God of Abraham and of Isaac and of Jacob." For Jacob is the old fleshly name of the man, isn't it? Jacob is called Israel only after his experience with God. But God is not ashamed to be called even the God of Jacob.

I think there is a lesson for us in that. God loved Jacob not because he was already Israel, but because he was Jacob. God loves you and me not for what we can become but just *because He loves us*. He does not ask that we be perfect; He does not ask that our characters be completely purified of all their worldly elements. He did not ask that of Jacob. Jacob was in many respects as despicable a character as you could hope to find; he was crafty and shrewd and cunning and deceptive and there were many other things that you could say about him. But Jacob was also a man who was true to the faith that had been given to him by his father; and God was true to the promise that He had made to Abraham. God will bless you and He will bless me, not for what we are, but for what He is, because He is God and because He has promised to be our God and the God and Father of our children. We should be deeply grateful to Him, as Jacob came to be, for all of His blessings, and we should serve Him faithfully and well.

CHAPTER IV

Joseph

JOSEPH is one of the most lovable characters in the Old Testament; his is one of the most beautiful and best-told stories in the Book, from the standpoint of literature and storytelling, as well as containing an abundance of religious and spiritual values. For the sake of continuity and understanding, suppose we divide the story of Joseph into four parts. First: the story of Joseph and his brothers, as it is told in Genesis 37.

Joseph was a lad of seventeen at that time, and like many seventeen-year-old children he was inclined to be conceited. He thought he was "pretty good"—he had some reason to think that—and he let his brothers and his father and mother know just how good he was. There is a chip-on-the-shoulder attitude here, a little of the "fresh-kid" attitude that you would like to take out of him. As you read the story you have at the beginning almost a feeling of antagonism against this young fellow, rather than sympathy for him; you feel as though he is getting, in a way, "what's coming to him."

First, there is the dream: "Now Joseph had a dream, and when he told it to his brothers they only hated him the more. He said to them, 'Hear this dream which I have dreamed: behold, we were binding sheaves in the field, and lo, my sheaf arose and stood upright; and behold, your sheaves gathered around it, and bowed down to my sheaf.'" Well, that is *not* one of the ways to win friends and influence people! The brothers "hated him yet more for his dreams and for his words." Then he dreamed another dream and said, "Behold I have dreamed another dream; and behold, the sun, the moon, and eleven stars were bowing down to me." When he told it to his father and his brothers, "his father rebuked him and said to him, 'What is this dream that you have dreamed? Shall I and your mother and your brothers indeed come to bow ourselves to the ground before you?' And his brothers were jealous of him, but his father kept the saying in mind" (37:5-11).

Much as you feel as though you would like to shake the boy for this display of conceit, you have to realize that there was, as in the case of Jacob, an element of parental fault. Go back a little further in the thirty-seventh chapter and read verse 3, "Now Israel [that is Jacob] loved Joseph more than any other of his children, because he was the son of his old age. . . ." I am not trying to excuse Joseph. I feel that he had something coming to him, and God apparently felt so too, and saw that he got it. But we must understand that Joseph was not entirely to blame; Jacob must at least share part of the blame for making a pet of the boy—and not only for making a pet of him, but for letting the rest of the family know that Joseph was the chosen.

Jacob made him a beautiful garment. The familiar translation is "a coat of many colors." The Hebrew does not say that; rather, it seems to suggest that it was a garment with long sleeves and long legs, or at least that it came down to his ankles. The exact color and shape we do not know; but we do know that it was an indication that this boy was favored above the others. And he was comparatively a newcomer to the family! The older brothers had already won their spurs, or thought they had; and to have this young upstart suddenly given a place of favor in his father's eyes, to have the sign of his father's favor flaunted before them every time he came out of the tent wearing that coat—this was "hard to take." But, as if that were not enough, then to have him dream those dreams and come and rub *that* in was still harder to take. So they plotted to get rid of him.

We read that they were "keeping the flock," and the father said to Joseph, "You go up and see how your brothers are getting along." I wonder why he was not already up there with them, helping to take care of the flock? He was old enough to be working. David was a shepherd long before he was seventeen. Perhaps this is another indication of some of the father's favoritism that was getting Joseph into trouble.

So Joseph went up to Shechem to find out what was going on. Now the family lived in the neighborhood of Hebron, and Hebron is about twenty miles south of Jerusalem; in Joseph's day, when walking was the only way to get there, it would have been a good day's travel. Shechem is near the mountains of Samaria (Gerizim and Ebal), thirty or forty miles north of Jerusalem; so that altogether it was a journey of two or three long days of hiking. And when he got there, he found that they had moved still farther north to the area of Dothan, which is another ten or fifteen miles north of Shechem. But you realize that in those days, when people were nomadic, when they pastured their flocks wherever they could find good pasture land, it was nothing for the nomad to roam over an area two or three hundred miles long, moving back and forth with the weather, hunting pasture land for his flock.[1]

Well, when they saw this young man coming (and of course he was wearing the blazer that his father had given him, proclaiming that he was his father's pet), they said, "Let's get rid of him; let's be done with this lord of dreams." They decided to kill him. But one of the brothers intervened and instead they put him in a pit and then sold him to a caravan that came along.

One of the points at which critics have attacked the credibility of the Old Testament is in the matter of the camels. There is mention of camels in the life of Abraham, and again here in the life of Joseph; but the critics tell us that camels had not been domesticated in that part of the world that early in history. But we now have proof to the contrary. Professor Cyrus Gordon points out that "the mention of camels here in Abraham's story and elsewhere in the patriarchal narrative, is often considered anachronistic. However, the correctness of the Bible is supported by the representation of camel-riding on seal cylinders of precisely this period from North Mesopotamia."[2]

There was a widespread commerce in that day across the Middle East, from Egypt up into Asia Minor among the Hittite peoples (or the Proto-Hittite peoples), and over into Mesopotamia. And that commerce had to go, as I suggested in our first chapter, through the area that we know as Palestine or "Canaan." There was no other way from Egypt to the Hittite country; they had to skirt the eastern end of the Mediterranean—which took them through Palestine. And there was no other safe road from Egypt to Mesopotamia. It would have been possible, of course, to cut straight across the desert. I flew across that route a few years ago and could see countless caravan tracks beneath the plane. But in the patriarchal period, it would have been extremely dangerous; and even today, desert raiders make the trip hazardous. So

---

[1] As a matter of fact, the nomad cattle-grazer in the Middle East still follows the same habits. Property lines, fences, even international boundaries are meaningless to the nomad.

[2] *Introduction to Old Testament Times,* p. 111. Gordon gives a reference to *Iraq* 6 (1939), plate II, 9. Cf. J. P. Free, "Abraham's Camels," *Journal of Near Eastern Studies* 3 (1944), pp. 187-193. It should be added that some recent scholars tend to lower Abraham's dates to about 1500 B.C., and the mention of the camel is taken as helping to confirm this date.

caravans made the long circuitous trip by way of the "Fertile Crescent" —the fertile strip along the edge of the desert. It was because these trade routes passed through Canaan that the cultural level of Canaan had been raised. It was not as high as in Egypt or Mesopotamia, but we make a serious mistake if we think of the people of Canaan as completely ignorant. According to Professor Albright, there were four, and possibly five different systems of writing used in Canaan in the patriarchal period.[3] In Joseph's day, Canaan may have been under the control of the Egyptians—I say, "may have been," only because we cannot locate Joseph's dates precisely.

Joseph was sold to one of the caravans, which was going in the direction of Egypt. They took him along and sold him on the slave market when they got there, according to Genesis 37:28. The other sons went back home to their father with Joseph's robe, which they had dipped in the blood of a goat they had killed, and said, "We found this; is it your son's robe or not?"—and let the father draw his own conclusions.

The second scene is Joseph in Egypt, which begins in the thirty-ninth chapter of Genesis, the thirty-eighth chapter being an interlude in the story, possibly for dramatic effect.

When was Joseph in Egypt? We found, when we were talking about Abraham, that we could not be certain of the year. The Bible, for this period, does not give us statements which can be positively equated with historical dates, and as a result, we have to allow a "margin of error" of about ten per cent in our calculations. We felt that the date of 2000 B.C., plus-or-minus two hundred years, was reasonable for Abraham. Joseph would, of course, have to be put about 290 years later, according to the Biblical chronology: in other words, about 1700 B.C.

Working in ancient history is like trying to fit together the pieces of a gigantic jigsaw puzzle. Those of us who are historians work with the pieces of history from the various data preserved for us on monuments, inscriptions, letters, etc., and when they *seem* to present a recognizable picture, we feel that we may have the solution. We do not claim to have *all* the pieces, nor do we claim to have placed the known pieces with perfect finality. Recognizing these limitations, we suggest that the picture of Joseph as presented in the Bible is most consistent with the facts of history if we put him in the period of the Hyksos.

[3] W. F. Albright, *The Archaeology of Palestine* (Pelican Books; Baltimore: Penguin Books, rev. 1954), pp. 185-190.

The Hyksos period in Egyptian history is called the "Second Inter-mediate Age," and dated 1780-1546 B.C. The name "Hyksos" was defined by the ancient historian Manetho as "shepherd kings," and this definition can still be found in many books. Modern scholars identify the word as meaning "rulers of foreign lands." The Thirteenth and Fourteenth Dynasties of Egypt had gotten into internal strife that had weakened the country, and then the foreign rulers came in (the Fiftheenth and Sixteenth Dynasties) and took over.[4]

These Hyksos were described by the Greek historians as Phoenician. In the light of modern knowledge it seems that they were Canaanites mixed with Indo-Europeans who had come from the north (perhaps the area we know as Russian Turkestan) in the sixteenth century B.C., invaded the Bible world and conquered it. They brought with them the horse and the chariot—the first time the horse is mentioned in this region. Interestingly enough, in pictures on Egyptian walls from this period the horse appears for the first time. Likewise, in Mesopotamia, the first time that we find any word for "horse" in the language is after the Hyksos' invasion. They also introduced the composite bow. They made a military nation out of Egypt, which up until that time had been peace loving; they made an internationally-minded people out of the Egyptians, who up until that time had been very much of a home-loving people. The historians say that the Hyksos, when they came into Egypt, took the narrow Egyptian view of the world and made it a world view. Before this, Egypt had been a great empire, but without foreign holdings; after this Egypt became a great empire with holdings in other parts of the world.

Now the Hyksos, having come from Canaan, not only had charge of Egyptian affairs, but also had supervision over Syria and Palestine. It seems likely that Joseph came into the country at that time. For that was a time when he could find those who were not too far distant in relationship from him, who could speak Semitic dialects, and whose names as we know from the Egyptian monuments were Semitic names. He would find more in common with them than he would with the Egyptians who hated the Semites. Moreover, the Hyksos had located their capital in the delta region at Avaris, and that checks with the fact that when Joseph was there the capital was

---

[4] For an interesting account, see G. Steindorff and K. C. Seele, *When Egypt Ruled the East* (Chicago: University of Chicago Press, 1942), Chap. III, "The Hyksos."

down in the delta region; likewise, when his father and his brothers and their flocks came and located in the land of Goshen, they were near the capital. The fact could only be fitted into the period of Egyptian history known as the Hyksos period. So our tentative date, based on Abraham's chronology, has some confirmation in history.

Joseph came to Egypt, and he was bought by Potiphar, the captain of the guard, and taken into his home. Before long he was tempted by Potiphar's wife—a story with which I am sure you are quite familiar. Joseph was handsome; his master's wife cast her eyes upon him, and said, "Lie with me!" But he refused and said to her, "Lo, having me my master has no concern about anything in the house, and he has put everything that he has in my hand; he is not greater in this house than I am; nor has he kept back anything from me except yourself, because you are his wife; how then can I do this great wickedness, and sin against God?" (39:6-9). Repulsed, she made her next move: she tried to discredit him by claiming that he had forced his attentions upon her. And Joseph was taken from the house and put in prison.

There is a parallel here, as students of Egyptian literature know, with the Egyptian story of "The Tale of the Two Brothers."[5] It is not as delicately told as is the story in the Bible; it is crude and sensual. Actually, there is very little reason, it seems to me, to claim that the Biblical story derives from the Egyptian. This is a situation that could and did occur often in the field of ancient literature. On the other hand, there is a delicacy in the Bible story which is amazing, and beautiful. Joseph is portrayed here in a color of fidelity to God and fidelity to the man for whom he is working.

In the fortieth chapter, there is a period of two years during which Joseph accomplished nothing. He did interpret the dreams of the chief butler and the chief baker, it is true, and he asked them to remember him when the dreams were fulfilled; but they forgot, as human beings do, and he remained in prison another two years. Then, "after two whole years, Pharaoh dreamed . . ."—Joseph was still in prison—and while Pharaoh was trying to get an interpretation for his dreams, the butler remembered about the time that he was in prison; he remembered how the young Hebrew had interpreted for him, and he called that to the attention of Pharaoh; Pharaoh sent for Joseph, and Joseph interpreted the dream.

[5] *Ancient Near Eastern Texts*, pp. 23-25.

These details are familiar to us, but to get the full picture we have to mention them, and piece them together. You remember that Pharaoh had two dreams, and that Joseph pointed out that they were the one and the same; that God had given the two dreams for the sake of emphasis, and so that Pharaoh would recognize the certainty of the prediction. The story of the seven fat cows and the seven lean cows, Joseph said, portrayed seven years of plenty and seven years of famine. Joseph not only told Pharaoh what was going to happen, but advised Pharaoh to store up during the years of plenty enough to take care of the years of famine. That made sense; so Pharaoh named Joseph the "food administrator" of the government, and gave him a place in Egypt second only to that of Pharaoh himself.

Notice the details in Genesis 41:41: "And Pharaoh said to Joseph, 'Behold I have set you over all the land of Egypt.' Then Pharaoh took his signet ring from his hand and put it on Joseph's hand, and arrayed him in garments of fine linen, and put a gold chain about his neck; and he made him to ride in the second chariot; and they cried before him, 'Bow the knee!'" (or *"ab rek!"* which may mean, "Bow the heart") a sign of obedience to Joseph.

The scene shifts; we read the story of how Jacob and his sons were faring during the famine back in the land of Canaan, and of the plan to go down to Egypt where there was plenty of food. I think perhaps it may be well to point out that the land of Egypt was usually the last land to have famine when famine came upon the Middle East. The rest of the Middle East depends largely upon rainfall for its food, and if there is a bad year, of course the food supply will be bad. But Egypt depends upon the flooding of the Nile, and the flooding of the Nile is determined by the rains and the snows in equatorial Africa and Abyssinia; and so it is very seldom that there is famine in the land of Egypt. Egypt always was the breadbasket of the Middle East and in Roman times was called the "granary of Rome."

So Jacob sent his sons down to Egypt to get food. It is a delightful story how they, the brothers, come to Joseph and bow down before him with their faces to the ground; how he sees and knows them, but treats them like strangers. He says, "From where do you come?" They tell him, "From the land of Canaan to buy food." He says, "You are spies, you have come to see the weakness of the land" (42:6-9). Then he asks about the family. He elicits the fact that they have a younger brother, Benjamin, who has stayed at home—and that sets the stage for the next step of the story.

Joseph gives them food only on one condition: one of the brothers must be left behind as a hostage and they are told that they will not have any chance of getting him back or of getting further food unless and until they bring young Benjamin to him. They go back home, and Jacob's sorrow is multiplied by the loss of yet another son. They reach the place where they must go back for more food; they just cannot hold out any longer. They start to argue that they must take Benjamin back, and Jacob says, "You have bereaved me of my children: Joseph is no more and Simeon is no more, and now you take Benjamin; all this is come upon me." Then Reuben says to his father, "Slay my two sons if I do not bring him back to you" (42:36-37). (He did not say, "Slay me!" but rather, "Take my two sons and kill them!" It is always simpler to sacrifice someone else!) But they are hungry again, and they have to go back for food, and they have to take Benjamin.

Once again the story is brilliantly told. "When Joseph saw Benjamin with them he said to the steward of the house, 'Bring the men into the house and slaughter an animal and make ready, for the men are to dine with me at noon'" (43:16). Then he receives them. He asks about the father. Finally he has food served to them, but he eats in another room. (That was typical Egyptian custom. One of the noteworthy facts about these chapters of Genesis is how true they are to all we know about Egyptian custom and Egyptian life. Whoever wrote this, whether Moses or an earlier author whose work Moses was led to use, it was written only by a person who knew Egypt and who knew Egyptian customs well.) They come in to sit down, and they are amazed because they are all seated in order of their rank. How would a stranger know their rank? And then Benjamin gets a portion five times greater than all the rest.

Once again Joseph has a little fun with them. He has their sacks filled with food, as much as they could carry. He has the money put in the top of the sacks again, as he had before, and then he has a silver cup put in the sack of the youngest brother, along with the money. And when they have gone a little way, he has some of his servants overtake them and say, "Why have you returned evil for good? Why have you stolen my silver cup?" Of course, they deny it: "Far be it from thy servants that they should do such a thing!" (44:7).

They open the sacks—and find the silver cup in Benjamin's! All the time, you see, the lesson is being driven home to the sons of Jacob that their deceptions have cost them dearly. They realize that they must return to Jacob without Benjamin, and they will have to tell him, "Benjamin has been taken away, and put to death." This they cannot stand: Judah cries that his father will die at the news. Nor can Joseph stand any more. He breaks down, has the room cleared and reveals himself to his brothers. He sends them to bring his father Jacob to Egypt; Pharaoh gives them all they need for the journey, and they go home, and tell the story to Jacob. God gives His permission, in a dream, for Jacob to go to his long-lost son in Egypt. And so Israel comes to the land of Egypt.

Now, consider the relation of Joseph to the promises of God. Joseph had come to Egypt at seventeen, and immediately began to exhibit a strong character. He refused the temptation of Potiphar's wife, because he could not wrong Potiphar and—what is more important —because he could not sin against God. Through all his life he remained true to the God of Israel. He understood that he was only an interpreter of dreams, but that God was the source of the dreams; that Pharaoh has not only dreamed, but that God has revealed the truth through them to Pharaoh.

Then, when Jacob died in Egypt, Joseph had him taken back to Canaan for burial, because Joseph knew that it was the will of the patriarchs that they be buried in the land that God had given them.

As he was drawing to the close of his earthly life (read Genesis 50:24, and the verses following), Joseph repeated the promises God had made to Abraham, to Isaac, and to Jacob, saying to his brothers, "I am about to die; but God will visit you, and will bring you up out of the land to the land which he swore to Abraham, to Isaac, and to Jacob." Then he bound the Israelites by an oath to carry his bones with them, upon their return, and to bury them in the land of Canaan. And so he was embalmed and placed in a coffin until the time should come that they could take him to the land of Canaan. When the author of the Book of Hebrews mentions the faith of Joseph, he emphasizes all this and says it is by faith that Joseph made mention of the Exodus "and gave directions concerning his bones" (Hebrews 11:22).

Where did Joseph get that faith? Jacob was partly to blame for the fact that Joseph was such a fresh young boy. But Jacob was also responsible for the religious faith that Joseph had. For seventeen years Joseph had lived in his father's home before he went to the land of Egypt. That was not long. Some of us who see our teen-agers go out from our homes into the world wonder how well they will stand up against the temptations and attractions of the world. Joseph is a good lesson for us. Here is a man who only had those few years in his father's house, but the years must have been well spent. The promises which God had made to Abraham and to Isaac and to Jacob had been deeply impressed upon the mind of young Joseph, and the moral teaching of the God of Israel must also have been deeply impressed upon him, for when he got down into Egypt he never forgot these things. You and I should take a great deal of courage from that as we bring up our own young folks, as we realize that God can use the training we give them at home to carry them over their years in the world.

CHAPTER V

Moses: The Man

In this chapter, we turn to the study of Moses, one of the greatest persons in the Old Testament. Abraham has three references made to him in the eleventh chapter of Hebrews; Moses has four. Moses is listed in the New Testament, I think, more times than any other Old Testament character. He stands in relation to the Old Testament prophets as Christ stands in relation to the apostles in the New Testament; he stands in relation to the people of God in the Old Testament as the Deliverer, the Saviour, without whom there would have been no Israel, without whom there would have been no deliverance from Egyptian bondage. In the Bible, there are some startling expressions used in connection with Moses. For example, in Exodus 14:31 ("the people . . . believed in the Lord and in his servant Moses"), faith in Moses is placed beside faith in the Lord; and in the New Testament (I Corinthians 10:2) there is the very remarkable statement that "all were baptized into Moses in the cloud and in the sea." Above all, Moses was privileged to stand with Jesus and Elijah on the Mount of Transfiguration (Matthew 17:3).

We shall make two studies of Moses, and we are going to divide these studies so that in this chapter we are thinking about the man and his background, and in the next chapter the man and the great work which God gave him to do.

The life of Moses can be divided very conveniently into three periods of forty years each. The first period of his life is the period in Pharaoh's house; following that, the period in Midian when he was really a refugee or an outcast from Egypt; and the third is the period of forty years as the leader and law-giver of Israel, chiefly in the wilderness.[1]

Of course you will ask, unless you know the Bible story, "How

---

[1] Much valuable material on Moses and his period can be found in Henry S. Noerdlinger, *Moses and Egypt: The Documentation to the Motion Picture, "The Ten Commandments"* (Los Angeles: University of Southern California Press, 1956), 202 pp.

did Moses come to be in Pharaoh's house? How did this Hebrew lad come to be in such a situation?" The story is found in the Book of Exodus in the first and second chapters. In Exodus 1:8 we read that ". . . there arose a new king over Egypt, who did not know Joseph." This king had grown tired of the Israelites who were too many in his land and too powerful, and he decided to do something to reduce their numbers. First he increased the amount of work they had to do and, when they seemed to thrive under that, he made it more difficult for them to make bricks by taking away the straw. Incidentally, in that connection, we ought to read very carefully what it says in the Scripture. I have seen all sorts of statements about making "bricks without straw," yet I am unable to find any place in the Bible where it says that is what they did. The straw was no longer furnished them as it had been; the suggestion is that they had not only to make the bricks, but they had to go out and gather the straw *for themselves,* and to do that without decreasing the number of bricks that they made. When the severe burden of heavy labor failed to accomplish its purpose, the king decided that the male babies of the Israelites should be put to death, and he passed the word to the Hebrew midwives that they should kill the Hebrew sons and let the daughters live. That failed, too. The midwives reported that the Hebrew women were too active for them, so that by the time they could get there, in attendance, the child was already born and hidden and they had no opportunity to kill it. Thereupon, Pharaoh commanded that every Hebrew baby boy was to be cast into the Nile (Exodus 1:22).

In the midst of all this turmoil and oppression, a child was born to a family in the house of Levi, and the mother planned to outwit the command of Pharaoh. As long as the child could be hidden, she hid it; then she took it and placed it in a little basket—"an ark," it is called in the Scripture—made of reeds and daubed with pitch. She placed the baby in the ark on the bank of the Nile at a spot where Pharaoh's daughter would come down to bathe and *see* the baby— thinking in the back of her mind, I suppose, that Pharaoh's daughter would be captivated by this little baby, as she was. Read on a little further in the second chapter and you find that the sister of this baby was waiting nearby—"at a distance"—and as soon as Pharaoh's daughter came and took the basket and saw the baby in it, the sister approached and said, "Shall I go and call you a nurse from the

Hebrew women to nurse the child for you?" And who is the nurse but the mother of the baby?

So the baby is in Pharaoh's daughter's home and the baby's mother is there to nurse and take care of him. The child was given a name at that time. He probably had been named by his parents previously, but now he was given a name by Pharaoh's daughter, and the name has come into English form as "Moses."

We read in Acts 7:22 that he was brought up "in all the wisdom of the Egyptians." That is a startling statement. It becomes more amazing as we think about what is involved in the wisdom of the Egyptians at that period.[2]

Moses certainly would have had some contact with the architectural splendors of Egypt,[3] although it is impossible for us to say just how much, for again the dates are not fully certain. If Moses was in Pharaoh's house when the capital was located in the delta region at Avaris (Tanis), then he may not have had opportunity to get into Upper Egypt (i.e., the southern portion), to see Luxor and Karnak. He may not even have seen Memphis and the pyramids. On the other hand, if the capital was located at Memphis, or possibly even at Amarna, then certainly he had often seen the pyramids; for they were a thousand years old before ever Moses had been born.

Moses knew something about writing, having been brought up in Pharaoh's house. He would doubtless have learned to read and to write, using the Egyptian system of hieroglyphs—those strange pictures which we know from the tombs and temples of Egypt. He may also have known something about the cuneiform (wedge-shaped) writing of Babylonia, for this was commonly used for international correspondence. You probably have heard of the "Tell el-Amarna letters," which were discovered in Egypt, and which date from the fifteenth century B.C. These letters represent the correspondence carried on by the Pharaoh of Egypt, the kings and petty kings of the Hittite Empire in Asia Minor, and the city kingdoms in the land of Canaan and Syria. This correspondence was not conducted in Egyptian or Hittite or Canaanite, but in Babylonian, which appears to have been the language of diplomacy of the day. It is also possible that Moses may have be-

---

[2] The following points are suggested in the article, "Moses," in *Harper's Bible Dictionary*, p. 461.

[3] For a good introductory survey, see C. Desroches-Noblecourt, *Le style égyptienne* (Paris: Librairie Larousse, 1946), 220 pp.

come acquainted with the alphabetic-type of writing which has been discovered at Serabit el-Khadem, not far from Mount Sinai.[4]

Not more than seventy-five years ago, Old Testament scholars were telling us that Moses could not possibly have written any part of the Old Testament, because no one knew how to write in those days! How unsound such a statement was we now know, for it is now clear that men were writing fully fifteen hundred years, possibly even two thousand years before the days of Moses. By the time Moses came on the scene, Egypt had a long history of writing and a great wealth of literature behind her.

It has been suggested that Moses was educated also in the wisdom of the Egyptian philosophers. Now the Egyptian philosophers were not like those of Greece; I would not want to suggest that there was any-body in any period of Egyptian history who would be equal to such Greek philosophers as Plato or Aristotle, Socrates or Zeno, or many more we might mention. But Egypt provided its own particular type of philosophy. It was a homey type, full of aphorisms similar to the proverbs which we find in the Bible. There were many proverbs about working hard and doing your job well: you would receive a reward if you did so; if you did not, you would get beaten with a rod, or something worse would happen to you.

Then there was considerable speculation on the world to come. Some-one has pointed out that, whereas the Babylonians seemed to be more interested in the past, the Egyptians were more interested in the future. The Babylonian literary remains contain many stories about creation, the flood, and other events (whether real or mythological) of the dis-tant past. The Egyptian literary remains contain writings such as the *Book of the Dead,* dealing with the concept of life after death, or the world to come. The writings of Ptah-hotep were probably among those that Moses studied, to judge from the fact that they are quoted over and over again by other Egyptian writers.

His knowledge of the wisdom of the Egyptians probably put Moses in close contact with the magicians and their magic. Now, I am not inclined to attribute the plagues which were brought upon Egypt at the word of Moses to his knowledge of Egyptian magic. We see clearly in the Scriptural record the difference between the works of Moses

[4] For a bare introduction to writing, see articles: "Writing" (pp. 828-831), "Cuneiform" (pp. 121-122), and "Serabit el-Khadem" (p. 663), in *Harper's Bible Dictionary* (New York: Harper & Brothers, 1952).

and the imitations of the magicians. He could do things they could not do, for he had the power of God. On the other hand, let us not forget the fact that for forty years Moses had been brought up in Pharaoh's house. If, as we shall see in a few pages, he was being trained for the high position of the Pharaoh, then certainly he was being indoctrinated in all of the ways of the Egyptians. He probably thought very little about the God of Israel, in those days—for the Lord had to tell Moses who He was, when He called him in Midian (Exodus 3:3-15).[5]

Moses may also have learned something about monotheism in the Egyptian court. The Pharaoh known originally as Amenhotep IV became a religious rebel, overthrowing the established worship and adopting the sole worship of the solar deity. At the same time, he took the name Ikhnaton,[6] and moved the capital to Akhetaton (present-day Tell el-Amarna). Now Ikhnaton's religious revolution did not last very long, and its roots were not deep-seated. Upon his death, his young son, Tut-ankh-aton (better known to us by the name of Tut-ankh-amun) was brought up in the old ways, the views of Ikhnaton were branded as heretical, and many of the things that he had written were effaced.

But you know that when men are so deeply moved by a heresiarch, they talk. And when men talk, the heresy that one would have hushed becomes bandied about. It is like a fire that only scatters as you try to beat it out. We know today about Ikhnaton's religious ideas simply because it was impossible to kill them. And so we suggest that Moses may have been influenced by these concepts of monotheism. He may have been thus providentially prepared for the revelation that God was to give him. At any rate, we know that the religious ideas which Moses passed on to all who read his Books are not the Egyptian concepts, but the truth revealed to Moses by God, in Midian, in the Exodus deliverance, and at Sinai.

Moses was brought up in the house of Pharaoh's daughter. Who was she? I wish we knew! If we work toward the period of Moses from one

[5] Some will doubtless say, "But if Moses was not faithful to the Lord in Egypt, why would the Lord call him?" This overlooks the entire Old Testament conception of sovereign election. God did not choose anyone at any time because of that person's fidelity, wisdom, or any other quality. God's election was sovereign—based only on His will. This is the Old Testament concept, illustrated repeatedly: Jacob, the Israelites, Saul, Amos, Isaiah, Jeremiah, and many others.

[6] Or Akhnaton, or Akhenaton, 1369-1353 B.C. Obviously, if we accept the 1446 B.C. for the Exodus, the observations of this paragraph become superfluous.

set of evidence, we arrive at a date somewhere in the middle of the fifteenth century—around 1446 B.C. If, on the other hand, we use other evidence, we arrive at a date early in the thirteenth century—about 1290 B.C. Contrary to the teachings of some Old Testament scholars, this is not simply a matter of taking the evidence of "either the Bible [I Kings 6:1 supports 1446 B.C., taken mathematically] or archaeology," but it is a complex question on which the Bible itself is ambiguous. We cannot go into all the details here, but we may note that mention of the city of Raamses and location in the delta in Exodus 1:11, is at least to be looked upon as having greater possibility in the time of Rameses II (thirteenth century) than in the time of Thutmose III (fifteenth century).

But if we tentatively accept the 1446 B.C. date of the Exodus, then it might be possible to identify Pharaoh's daughter with the famous queen (she called herself "king") known as Hatshepsut (1486-1468 B.C.). She was the one who prided herself on being the first to restore the Egyptian temples after the Hyksos; she was more interested in Egypt's internal splendor than in external conquests. She built the beautiful Deir el-Bahri. She had obelisks cut from the granite quarries at Asswan and erected at Karnak. She renewed operations at the turquoise mines in Sinai and sent maritime expeditions to Punt.[7]

But whoever the daughter of Pharaoh may have been, Moses was brought up in her house, and, according to Josephus (the great Jewish historian who lived in the first century A.D.), he could have become Pharaoh. The line of succession in Egypt did not pass from father to son, but it went down through the oldest daughter. If the daughter of Pharaoh who took the baby Moses into her home was the oldest daughter of the reigning Pharaoh, and if Moses was the oldest son in her house, this would fit with what Josephus tells us. It is not beyond the realm of possibility that when Moses chose to throw in his lot with the people of God, he was renouncing all claim to the throne of Egypt. The writer of the book of Hebrews says that it was by faith that Moses chose to be reckoned with the people of God rather than to be counted as Pharaoh's daughter's son (Hebrews 11:24-25).

The second part of Moses' life was in Midian—and again you ask

[7] The fascinating story of Hatshepsut can be found in J. A. Wilson, *The Culture of Ancient Egypt (Phoenix Books,* P-11; Chicago: University of Chicago Press, 1956), pp. 169-177. This book was originally published under the title, *The Burden of Egypt* (1951). For Egyptian chronology I am following Wilson.

the question, "How did he get *there*?" The story is told in the second chapter of Exodus: "One day, when Moses had grown up, he went out to his people and looked on their burdens, and he saw an Egyptian beating a Hebrew, one of his people. He looked this way and that, and seeing no one he killed the Egyptian and hid him in the sand. When he went out the next day, behold two Hebrews were struggling together; and he said to the man that did the wrong, 'Why do you strike your fellow?' He answered, 'Who made you a prince and a judge over us? Do you mean to kill me as you killed the Egyptian?' Then Moses was afraid, and he thought, 'Surely the thing is known.' When Pharaoh heard of it, he sought to kill Moses. But Moses fled from Pharaoh, and stayed in the land of Midian" (Exodus 2:11-15).

Why did he choose on this occasion to align himself with the Hebrews? When we find him in Midian at the well of Jethro, he is "an Egyptian." He could have passed anywhere as an Egyptian. Why did he choose on this particular occasion to reveal himself as one of the Hebrew people? Go back and read the story again, in the first part of the second chapter, and see how the mother of the child was taken to be his nurse, and how she brought him to Pharaoh's daughter. The training of Moses in the earliest days of his childhood was under the tutelage of his own mother, a Hebrew woman; and she did her job so well that forty years later, when the time came for him to decide whether he would be on the side of the Egyptians or the Hebrews, he chose, it seems, without hesitation to be numbered with the people of God.

This is, in my opinion, a significant lesson, and one of the great truths of Scripture. In the Hebrew society, the home is central, and in the home, the knowledge of the Lord. A mother's greatest work is to bring her children up that they may know the Lord. The woman who has already raised her children, or the woman who has no children, may find her career outside of the home. But no career, in my opinion, can possibly be greater than that of a mother bringing up her children to walk in the way of the Lord. I think one of the reasons why we have such moral deficiency among today's children is the fact that so many of today's mothers have made the home, and the training that should be part of the home, matters of secondary importance. Moses' mother did her job well, and it stood up under test forty years later.

We next find Moses in Midian with Jethro the priest. In Jethro's household he got his wife Zipporah (21:2), and from her his sons

Gershom and Eliezer. It may well be that from Jethro he learned a great deal about the worship of Jehovah. Moses, even though he had had a Hebrew mother to train him for the first few years of his life, left her to go into training in Pharaoh's house, and I doubt very much that he got any Hebrew religious training there; it is far more likely that he was trained in all of the polytheism of the Egyptians. Jethro is portrayed in the eighteenth chapter of Exodus as a worshiper of the Lord. It may well be that the knowledge of Jehovah was part of his heritage, and that in his household, Moses came to realize more about what the worship of Jehovah involves.[8] From Jethro he also got wise counsel, when the cares and the burdens of the people were upon him; Jethro warned him that he could not carry this load alone, and advised him to appoint others and turn the details over to them and just handle main policy matters. We therefore can attribute to Jethro uncommon "common sense," and we can assume that Moses may have had many occasions, during the forty years in Midian, to learn from Jethro.

While Moses was in Midian, he also had plenty of opportunity as a shepherd to learn the roads and the sources of water supply and all those other details that he would need when the time came to lead the people of God through the wilderness on a thirty-eight-year march. You just don't go out into a wilderness with a large group without any knowledge of the terrain. You could get lost and die—simply because of insufficient water. But Moses knew the area; he had spent forty years there.

The third part (and we will go over this rather quickly because we are going to talk more about it in our next chapter) shows us Moses with the people of Israel. This story divides naturally into five main scenes.

First of all there was the appearance of God in the burning bush, when God called him out of the life of a shepherd in Midian to go back and free his people from the awful oppression that had fallen upon them in the land of Egypt (Exodus 3).

Then there was the contest with Pharaoh in the fifth and the following chapters of the book of Exodus down to chapter twelve, which ends with the plagues upon the Egyptians and the death of the first-born of each house in Egypt.

[8] Jethro, we should remember, was a Midianite, and Midian, according to Genesis 25:1-2, was a son of Abraham by Keturah.

Next, there was the great and terrible deliverance told in the twelfth chapter of Exodus. By a mighty hand, the Lord led His people out of Egypt through the waters of the Red Sea (or the "Sea of Reeds"), into the wilderness and up to the foot of Mt. Sinai.

The fourth scene gives us that magnificent moment at Mt. Sinai when God chose to speak with Moses face to face. He spoke to other men only in figures and in dreams and in images, but with Moses, face to face. No other man ever had that privilege here on earth until the day that our Lord came to walk among men.

The last scene is a touching one. Moses, the old man, stands on Mt. Nebo looking out across the Dead Sea and over to the hills of the Promised Land, and he sees at hand the realization of the promise which God had made to Abraham so many years before. This people, which originally consisted of Abraham and Isaac and Jacob and Jacob's boys, and which was now a great multitude that had been led through the wilderness by Moses for all these years, stood poised and ready to go in and take possession of the place which God had promised. But Moses himself could not go in.

This is one of the most interesting points of the story. Things like this should give us new incentive in our own Bible study and in our own Christian lives, because we find that even the greatest of Old Testament characters are just human beings. Moses was a man. He was not a god. He was a *great* man, perhaps the greatest man of the Old Testament; but he was a *man,* and he got tired and irritated with these people who were so stubborn and backsliding, and he seems even to have lost his temper with God at times. And God said to him, "For that you cannot go in." Moses had to stand there and look into the Promised Land from afar, because once he had doubted God's word.

You and I will probably never have the opportunity to be great leaders of God's people, in the sense that Moses was. There doesn't *have* to be another Moses in this world, any more than there has to be another Jesus Christ. He served the people of God for the purpose for which God had called him. But God *does* need men and women who will be faithful in the particular task that He gives them. Sometimes they lose the blessing simply because they do not have enough faith; simply because they talk back to God in their doubt. We can learn from Moses' weakness and from his humanity to trust God, take Him at His word, and then we will have the joy of seeing what God intends to accomplish.

There are other truths that we can draw from Moses' life. We certainly can draw the lesson of the great choice which each one has to make between the world, represented by Pharaoh's household and the wealth of Egypt, and God. Moses had Egypt at his feet at a moment in Egyptian history when to be Pharaoh would have been to be one of the great characters of history; yet he chose to be God's man with God's people.

It was a terrible choice to have to make, but he made it and he made it gladly. You and I, too, should make our choice to be on God's side, no matter what we have to give up.

CHAPTER VI

Moses: The Servant

IN OUR LAST chapter we studied Moses in the light of the things that happened to him. In this chapter we will study him from a different angle: that of the servant of God, in his relation to Pharaoh, in his relation to the people of Israel, and, finally, in his relation to God. Let us see first how he looks standing side by side with Pharaoh.

Moses grew up in Pharaoh's court, as we have already mentioned, and may have been heir to the Egyptian throne. But he was forced by events and circumstances, by his own choice, and by the will of God to oppose Pharaoh. He spent years in hiding, then returned from Midian to Egypt to lead his people out of that "house of bondage," the first step in the fulfillment of God's promise to give them the land of Canaan where they were to become a great nation. The story is told in Exodus, chapters seven through twelve, and is concerned chiefly with the account of the plagues. We shall not discuss the plagues; I am sure that most of you are quite familiar with that part of the story, in which Moses performed one miracle after another, by the power of God, until at last Pharaoh let his people go.[1]

One thing is remarkable in all this: the singleness of purpose which we find in the man Moses. As he comes into conflict with Pharaoh, he has chance after chance to compromise, to settle for a little less. But he never compromises; committed completely to God, he will settle for nothing less than the unconditional release of his people and their property. Let us read over some of the account in this section of Exodus.

In Exodus 8:25, Pharaoh began to realize that he was up against a situation that was becoming too much for him. There had been four

[1] There is a marked tendency today to treat the plagues as natural phenomena. While I do not deny that God could, and on many occasions did, use natural phenomena in ways that seem to us to be "miraculous," I find the psychological elements of Exodus 7–12 difficult, if not impossible, to account for on that basis. These people, who knew Egypt and its seasons and problems, were forced to admit that Moses' God was working against the gods of Egypt—which is to say, contrary to nature, or supernatural.

plagues, and against all of them Pharaoh had been helpless. So he offered a compromise: the Israelites could worship their Lord, if they wished, *but within the borders of Egypt*. Moses refused the bait; it would only cause trouble with the Egyptian people. Firmly he replied: "We must go three days' journey into the wilderness and sacrifice to the Lord our God as he will command us" (8:27). Then Pharaoh offered to let the men of Israel go. Moses would not settle for that either: "We will go with our young and our old; we will go with our sons and our daughters and with our flocks and herds, for we must hold a feast to the Lord" (10:9).

Pharaoh tried again: he would let all the *people* go, all the adults and children; but the flocks and herds of Israel were to remain in Egypt. That probably seemed to him quite reasonable. Here was Moses' chance to get out, at a comparatively small cost: he need only leave their possessions behind. But God had promised Moses that when they left Egypt they would take their possessions along. What was more, they would demand and get from their Egyptian taskmasters the wages due them for all those years, all those generations of bondage. It was that, or more plagues! It took courage for Moses to stand up to Pharaoh—courage and faith. Finally, the climax was reached: the plague of the death of the first-born in all the land. Not a home escaped—for there must be a first-born in every household! Without waiting for morning, Pharaoh sent for Moses and Aaron, and gave them the exit clearance. Moses had won! The Israelites left Egypt with all they had demanded, and passed safely across the Red Sea, leaving the hosts of Pharaoh floundering, drowning, in its waters.

Moses is equally inspiring in his relation to the people of Israel. We have already mentioned the choice made by Moses, when he came to his adult life, to take the side of his people. He saw an Egyptian beating a Hebrew, and he killed the Egyptian and hid his body in the sand (see Exodus 2:11).

Now, I am not sure that what he did was right. It is not so much because he killed the Egyptian that I find fault with him, but rather because he took into his own hands the deliverance of his people. Instead of calling upon God to save the people, instead of waiting for God to do something about it, Moses sought by his own effort, by his own might, by his own wisdom, to free his people from bondage. To me, that is the major sin; that is even more of a sin than killing a man. He did something that only God had the right to do.

Then, after he had been in Midian for a while, and after he had had the vision of the burning bush (which we will consider later), he went back to Egypt, where he and his brother Aaron gathered together the elders of the people of Israel. Aaron was the spokesman. Moses had complained, you remember, that he was a stutterer and therefore not able to speak and God had given him Aaron to be his mouthpiece. So when Moses had gathered the people together, Aaron declared what the Lord had spoken to Moses, and "the people believed; and when they heard that the Lord had visited the people of Israel and that he had seen their affliction, they bowed their heads and worshiped" (4:31).

Here is an indication of the leadership potential of Moses; he was able to gather around him the elders of the people of Israel, who by this time had been in Egypt many years. The Hebrew text of Exodus 12:40 indicates that Israel had been in Egypt 430 years; on the other hand, the Samaritan and the Septuagint texts indicate that the 430 was divided into two parts, each of 215 years.[2] At any rate, whether it was 215 or 430, it was a long time. When a people settles down for 215 years, it is pretty hard to rekindle the pioneer enthusiasms. Yet Moses was able to fire the imagination of these people and elders of Israel; he was able to convince them that God was bent upon their deliverance, and he made them follow him. That is leadership!

Notice three facts about this relationship between Moses and the people of Israel. First of all, notice the long suffering which Moses had undergone for his people, and his willingness not once, but many times to intercede on their behalf when they were about to be visited by God with some punishment. The Book of Numbers is the story of the rebellion of the people, of the seeming desire of God to wipe them out, and of Moses' continued insistence that they should have another chance. But before we turn to the Book of Numbers, there is one other scene we must study, in the thirty-second chapter of Exodus.

As Moses was coming down from the mountain, having received the law from God, God told him that he was facing a bad situation. "'They have turned aside quickly out of the way which I commanded them;—said God—they have made for themselves a molten calf, and

---

[2] Textual students will recognize at once the strength of evidence of the Samaritan agreeing with the Septuagint. Further, Galatians 3:17 seems to support the 215+215 scheme, for the 430 years are from the covenant of Abraham to the giving of the Law.

have worshiped it and sacrificed to it. . . .' And the Lord said to Moses, 'I have seen this people, and behold, it is a stiff-necked people; now therefore let me alone, that my wrath may burn hot against them and I may consume them; but of you I will make a great nation' " (32:8-10). Moses might have replied, "All right . . ."—he was tired of these people, too, by this time—"go ahead, wipe them out." But that is not Moses. Instead, he answered, " 'O Lord, why does thy wrath burn hot against thy people . . . ? Why should the Egyptians say, "With evil intent did he bring them forth to slay them in the mountains, and to consume them from the face of the earth"? Remember Abraham, and Isaac, and Israel . . .' " (32:11-13). And the Lord repented and gave them another chance.

Now turn to the Book of Numbers, chapter 14. After the spies had gone out to look over the land of Canaan, they came back and gave their report on the people of the land; it was a wonderful land, flowing with milk and honey—they brought back a huge bunch of grapes carried on a big stick by two of them, to show what the land was like— but they said the people there were big, too, and the Israelites were as grasshoppers in their sight. They would not have a chance against such giants. And God again displayed His displeasure with the lack of faith on the part of these people. "And the Lord said to Moses, 'How long will this people despise me? And how long will they not believe in me, in spite of all the signs which I have wrought among them? I will strike them with the pestilence and disinherit them, and I will make of you a nation greater and mightier than they' " (Numbers 14:11-12). And again Moses pleaded for his people: " 'The Lord is slow to anger, and abounding in steadfast love, forgiving iniquity and transgression. . . .' Pardon the iniquity of this people, I pray thee, according to the greatness of thy steadfast love [or mercy], and according as thou hast forgiven this people from Egypt even until now" (14:18-19). Again God spared the people.

A little later, we read the account of the rebellion of the sons of Korah (Numbers 16). God was once more about to visit the people with punishment, and He told Moses and Aaron to separate themselves from the congregation, "that I may consume them in a moment." Moses and Aaron fell on their faces and prayed, ". . . shall one man sin, and wilt thou be angry with *all* the congregation?" So the punishment fell only upon the sons of Korah. But there were others who had been involved in this rebellion. They, too, must be punished so God told Moses, "Get away from the midst of this congregation, that I may consume them . . ." (16:45). But Moses and Aaron rushed into the crowd and divided it, and they stood between those who had already been smitten with the punishment of God, and those who were to be preserved because of Moses' insistence that they be spared. For less than this men have been cited for courage "above and beyond the call of duty"!

Then, there had been lack of food and water, and the people murmured and rebelled again, and the Lord sent fiery serpents to smite them (Numbers 21:4-6). Once again Moses interceded and rescued them. Only once in all the wilderness journey, only *once* did Moses seem to lose his patience, and that is in the story in the twentieth chapter of Numbers where he smote the rock in impatience to bring forth the water for them. He was, indeed, a man of long-suffering and faith and intercession!

The second thing I would like to emphasize about Moses in his relationship to the people of Israel is his responsibility for their worship. Through God he was led to set up the Tabernacle and arrange its worship. The worship of the Jew today, and, to a certain extent, the worship of the Christian, stems back to Moses and the Tabernacle.

The third fact I would note is this: Moses gave them the Scriptures. So far as we know, the first Scriptures were written in the days of Moses. There were stories, probably even written records, before that time that have come down to us in the Bible, but Moses was the one who kept detailed records of the encampments, records of the events and some of the battles that were fought (Numbers 33). He gave the children of Israel the written statute of laws ("the Book of the Covenant") mentioned in the twenty-fourth chapter of Exodus. He kept a copy of his farewell address mentioned in the thirty-first chapter of Deuteronomy; and I believe that practically the whole Book of Deuteronomy is that farewell address. These things were the beginning of what we now call "the Bible"; and well are the first five books of the Bible called the Books of Moses, because he is the one who gave to Israel, and through them to us, the beginnings of sacred Scripture.[3]

[3] To argue that "unless Moses wrote the entire Pentateuch, we can no longer speak of Mosaic authorship" is, in my opinion, an unjustified extension of the truth. If we can say that "grace and truth came by Jesus Christ," even though He did not write a single word of the Gospels, certainly we can say that "the Law came by Moses." If we can say that "Moses spoke all these words," even if it was Aaron's mouth that actually did the speaking—and this is what the

Turn your thoughts now to the relationship between Moses and God, and think of it in three scenes.

First of all there was the great experience of the burning bush, when Moses was in Midian keeping the flocks of his father-in-law Jethro. Moses saw a bush and it seemed to be burning, but when he drew near to it, he found that it was not consumed. Then the angel of the Lord appeared and spoke to him. Essentially, this is a repetition of the covenant made to Abraham, plus the promise of God to deliver Israel from the Egyptians and bring them into the land of Canaan, where the covenant which God had made with their fathers would at last be fulfilled. There is also a revelation to Moses concerning the name of the Lord. When Moses said, "If . . . they [the people] ask me, 'What is his name?' what shall I say to them?" God answered, "I am who I am"[4] (Exodus 3:13-14). Thus the name "Jahweh"—or "Jehovah," as we know it in English—comes to be the *covenant* name; it is the name for God specifically as He stands in relation to Israel.

The power of God is also revealed and made available to Moses. In Exodus 4, when Moses feared to go back to Egypt because the people might not listen to him, the Lord said, "What is that in your hand?" He said, "A rod." God said, "Cast it on the ground." And it became a serpent, and Moses fled from it. Then the Lord said to Moses, "Take it by the tail"; and it became a rod in his hand. This was done for a purpose: when Moses got back to Egypt he could prove that he was acting not on his own authority, but on the authority of God.

When Moses expressed hesitation because he stuttered, God gave him a spokesman, Aaron. The next words are important: "And you shall speak to him and put the words in his mouth; and I will be with your mouth and with his mouth, and will teach you what you shall

---

Bible teaches—then we can say "Moses wrote these words," even though God may have used someone else to give us the final written form. What we need to insist upon is: (1) the historicity and veracity of the Pentateuch, (2) the essential Mosaic authorship, and (3) the plenary inspiration of the Holy Spirit for the Pentateuch in the form in which God caused it to be finally inscripturated.

[4] "Yahweh" (or Jahweh) is usually taken to be derived from the root $hwh=hyh$, meaning "to be." Whether it is to be read as "I am," "I shall be," or "I cause to be," it is almost impossible to say. More recently an effort to derive the word from the root hwy, "to say," (cf. Ugaritic hwt, "word") has gained some support. While at first glance this does not seem to be compatible with the Scriptural "I am," it does fit well with the concept of the "Word." The name, in the last analysis, is as mysterious as God Himself.

do. *He shall speak for you to the people: and he shall be a mouth for you, and you shall be to him as God*" (Exodus 4:15-16). Add to them the words in Exodus 7:1, *"See, I make you as God to Pharaoh; and Aaron your brother shall be your prophet."* Here we have one of the most important definitions of a prophet: he is God's mouth. When Moses spoke, Aaron was to say to the people what Moses said to him. This is what a prophet is supposed to do: to tell the people whatever God has told him.

That great vision, that call at the burning bush, is what sent Moses back to his people, and enabled him to lead them to freedom.

The next scene finds God and Moses at Sinai. The record begins in Exodus 19 and continues through the rest of Exodus. The people arrive at the foot of the mountain three months after leaving Egypt, and God commands them to stay there at the foot of the mountain while Moses goes up to receive the law.

Following this, we have a long series of revelations of God to Moses. In the twenty-fourth chapter of Exodus, Moses has a vision of glory; it is one of the things that you may have overlooked. I do not know how many times I read this before it stood out on the page as I had not seen it before: "Then Moses and Aaron, Nadab and Abihu, and seventy of the elders of Israel went up, and they saw the God of Israel; and there was under his feet as it were a pavement of sapphire stone, like the very heaven for clearness" (24:9-11). Moses was not the only one to go up into the mountain. Seventy-three others went with him and saw God. But Moses alone had the privilege of speaking with God face to face, so that when he came down from the mountain, his face was shining, and the people saw the glory and the splendor of God in its radiance (Exodus 34).

One day, when Moses' brother and sister, Aaron and Miriam, began to complain because of the place that Moses seemed to be taking to himself in Israel, God said to them, "Hear my words: If there is a prophet among you, I the Lord make myself known to him in a vision, I speak with him in a dream. Not so with my servant Moses; he is entrusted with all my house. With him I speak mouth to mouth clearly, and not in dark speech: and he beholds the form of the Lord" (Numbers 12:6-8). Moses is the one person in the Old Testament who had the privilege which was given to no other—the privilege of face-to-face communion with God.

Then we come to the final scene, on the mountain of Moab, Mount

Nebo, just before the death of Moses. To understand it, we must go to Numbers 20, where the people rebelled because they did not have enough food and water, and where God commanded Moses to strike the rock that the water might come forth. Moses was tired. He had had the burden of these people for many years; he had seen rebellion upon rebellion, when they had lacked the faith to go ahead in the promises of God. "And Moses and Aaron gathered the assembly before the rock, and he said to them, 'Hear now, you rebels; shall we bring forth water for you out of this rock?' And Moses lifted up his hand and struck the rock with his rod twice; and water came forth abundantly . . ." (Numbers 20:10-11).

Some say that the sin here was in striking the rock twice; once would have been enough. That may be. But it seems to me that there is a greater sin in what Moses *said*: "Shall *we* bring forth water out of the rock?" Just once, it seems, Moses presumed to take his place on a par with God—and you can hardly blame him, with all of the experiences he had had—but just this once he seems to take to himself more than he should have. *He* was not bringing any water out of the rock; God was doing it through him. "Shall *we* bring forth water?" For that, he is told that he is not going to see the promised land.[5]

"The Lord said to Moses, 'Go up into this mountain of Abarim, and see the land which I have given to the people of Israel. And when you have seen it, you also shall be gathered to your people, as your brother Aaron was gathered, because you rebelled against my word in the wilderness of Zin during the strife of the congregation . . .'" (Numbers 27:12-14).

Moses accepted the will of God in this respect just as he had accepted it in every other respect. God had said, "You cannot go into the land." Moses was content to ask, "Well, then, let me go up and *look* at it." And he went up to the top of a high peak there on the Transjordanian plateau east of the Dead Sea, where, on a clear day, you can see not only all of the southern end of Palestine, and Jerusalem there on a hilltop very clearly, but you can see the full length of the Jordan Valley, and miles beyond, a hundred miles and more. On a rare day,

[5] I was asked, after this statement had been made, if Moses did not go to heaven just because of this one mistake. This indicates how careless we become with Scriptures. The "Promised Land" is not heaven; it is Canaan. It is not even a type of heaven, for it had to be won, it was full of sin, and the People were later exiled from it into Babylonia. That Moses did go to heaven is clear from Matthew 17:3 and Hebrews 11:23-28, 39-40.

you can even see the snow-capped peaks of Mt. Hermon.[6] ". . . Moses went from the plains of Moab to Mount Nebo, to the top of Pisgah, which is opposite Jericho. And the Lord showed him all the land, Gilead as far as Dan, all Naphtali, the land of Ephraim and Manasseh, all the land of Judah as far as the Western Sea, the Negeb, and the Plain, that is, the valley of Jericho the city of the palm trees, as far as Zoar. And the Lord said to him, 'This is the land which I swore to Abraham, and to Isaac, and to Jacob, "I will give it to your descendents." I have let you see it with your eyes, but you shall not go over there'" (Deuteronomy 34:1-4). Moses died there in the land of Moab, and we read that he was buried according to the word of the Lord, in the valley of the land of Moab. And no man knows the place of his burial to this day.

What lessons can we take from Moses for our own lives? Well, certainly we can take a lesson in faith: here is a man with tremendous faith. We can certainly take a lesson in obedience: he did what God told him to do, although at times it was at awful cost and at fearful risk. We can take a lesson in service: here is a man who for long years spent himself in the service of God on behalf of his people. And we can take a lesson in prayer: Moses prayed again and again and again for his people. We too, perhaps even more than Moses because we have Jesus Christ to intercede for us, can pray that God will spare His people.

[6] For a well-written description of this view in a popularized book, see Werner Keller, *The Bible as History* (London: Hodder & Stoughton, 1956), p. 153.

CHAPTER VII

Joshua

JOSHUA is known to us as the successor of Moses; he is the man who in the providence of God had the privilege of fulfilling the promise which God had made so long ago, to Abraham.

Four hundred years earlier, God had promised Abraham that He would give him a country. He called him out of Ur of the Chaldeans to go to another country which He would give him, and which would be the homeland of his seed, a numerous seed, as numerous as the sands of the sea or the stars of heaven. Abraham never lived to see that fulfilled; he was only a visitor, a sojourner in the land. He was told by God that it would not be his, that four hundred years later his descendants would occupy the country. Now, with Joshua, the promise is about to be fulfilled. That in itself ought to give us cause for consideration and for thanksgiving that God does not neglect His promises. Sometimes you and I feel that God has forgotten us because we do not get the answer to our prayers, perhaps in a few days or even for weeks or months. With the Israelites, it was not a matter of days or weeks or months but of generations and centuries before God fulfilled His promise. But He fulfilled it. Our God is a promise-keeping God.

Why did God use Joshua, and what is there here that will be of help to us in our Christian lives?

First of all, there was preparation. Few men, if any, step into responsible positions without preparation. Sometimes in our shortsightedness we seem to get the idea in regard to Bible characters that they come on the scene ready-made, fully prepared; here they are, God's gift to the world! They take up the work, and that is all there is to it. But if you will read more carefully you will find that usually—I think we could even say always—there is a period of preparation behind them. God lays His plans well in advance. Joshua, for instance, does not come on the scene at the crossing of the Jordan and Jericho; he had already come on the scene forty years before that.

He is described as an Ephraimite (that is, of the tribe of Ephraim) and the son of Nun. In Exodus 17:8-16, we find him at Rephidim, when the Amalekites came to fight against Israel: "And Moses said to Joshua, 'Choose for us men, and go out, fight with Amalek; tomorrow I will stand on the top of the hill with the rod of God in my hand.'" Joshua was in command of this minor skirmish; you see, already he was a man that Moses could call upon.

He was Moses' personal minister. When God told Moses to go up to the mountain where He would give him the tables of stone we are told: "Moses rose, with his servant Joshua, and Moses went up into the mountain of God" (Exodus 24:13). Joshua was Moses' personal attendant at the time that he was given the command to go to Sinai. There is some question as to whether Joshua had the privilege of being on Sinai with Moses, but he certainly was with him before he went up and after he came down; it would seem that Joshua had accompanied him part of the way, because "when Joshua heard the noise of the people as they shouted, he said to Moses, 'There is a noise of war in the camp!'" (Exodus 32:17).

Moses used to pitch the tent of meeting outside the camp, and then go out to that tent to receive instruction from the Lord. All of the men of Israel would stand in the doors of their tents and watch him as he went there. They would see the pillar of cloud come down upon the tent as Moses held his communion with God. Now notice: "when Moses turned again into the camp, his servant Joshua, the son of Nun, a young man, did not depart from the tent" (33:11). Even in the worship of Moses, Joshua was in attendance.

There came a time when a committee of twelve was sent into the land of Canaan to investigate conditions there and to see whether it was possible for the Israelites to move up from the south through the most logical entrance into the land of Canaan. Joshua was selected as one of that committee. At the time he was forty years of age, and already he had been with Moses for a year or two as his personal minister. The twelve spies went up and took a look at the land of Canaan and when they came back the majority were of the opinion that they could not go in and take the land, that the people there were too big for them. Two of the spies did not agree with that report: Joshua the son of Nun and Caleb the son of Jephunneh. In a minority report, they called upon the congregation of Israel to act on faith, to believe that God would lead them into the land and give it to them, and they begged them not to rebel against the Lord in unbelief. When the people rejected Joshua's report, God said quite bluntly that "Not one shall come into the land where I swore that I would make you dwell, except Caleb the son of Jephunneh and Joshua the son of Nun" (Numbers 14:30). The rest of them, for their faithlessness, were condemned not to enter the land, and the ten spies who brought back the false report were consumed by a plague from the Lord for their complete unbelief.

Joshua was ordained by Moses. "And the Lord said to Moses, 'Take Joshua the son of Nun, a man in whom is the spirit, and lay your hand upon him; cause him to stand before Eleazar the priest and all the congregation, and you shall commission him in their sight. You shall invest him with some of your authority, that all the congregation of the people of Israel may obey. And he shall stand before Eleazar the priest, who shall inquire for him by the judgment of the Urim before the Lord; at his word they shall go out, and at his word they shall come in, both he and all the people of Israel with him, the whole congregation'" (Numbers 27:18-21). Moses did as the Lord commanded. Then, near the end of the Book of Deuteronomy we read, "And the Lord said to Moses, 'Behold, the days approach when you must die; call Joshua, and present yourselves in the tent of meeting that I may commission him.'" So ". . . the Lord commissioned Joshua the son of Nun and said, 'Be strong and of good courage; for you shall bring the children of Israel into the land which I swore to give them: I will be with you'" (Deuteronomy 31:14-23). Joshua was not only ordained by Moses; he was also ordained by God.

That is the background. To take up the study of Joshua at the crossing of the river Jordan, just as they were ready to go into the land, without understanding that background, is to strip from the story many of its most important details. This man had had a record of faithful service and strong faith; he had had an experience in which he stood against the majority with his minority report; he had had the background of service under Moses as Moses' own personal minister; he had entered into some of the great religious experiences of Moses from time to time during that period: all this is vitally important. Now the time comes that he is to take over the leadership of the people and lead them into the land of Canaan.

Just prior to the death of Moses, there was a census of the people and it was disclosed that all of those who had been in Egypt had now died off, with the exception of Joshua and Caleb (cf. Numbers 26, especially verse 64). In other words, that generation which God swore would not enter into the land because of unbelief had passed away. So the situation is such that they can move forward: the new generation can go in. The only one remaining who does not have that privilege is Moses himself.

Joshua rises, here, to his full stature. He takes command. He gathers his host on the banks of Jordan, and cries to them, "Sanctify yourselves; for tomorrow the Lord will do wonders among you!" (Joshua 3:5).

On the banks of *Jordan!* Let us try to visualize it. There is no other river like it in all the world.[1] On either side of the valley are mountains, two thousand feet high and more. These drop rather suddenly to the valley, which is a great trench, five to thirteen miles wide. At Jericho it is the widest. But the river itself lies within another valley within the valley. The larger depression, which slopes gradually downward from the foot of the mountains to the river valley, is called by the Arabs "the Ghôr"; it is for the most part barren and flat: roads on either side of the river are on this portion. Jericho is a beautiful oasis of green in the dreary dust-brown of the Ghôr. The Jordan has cut a deeper trench within the Ghôr, which the Arabs call "the Zôr." At places, this is 150 feet deeper than the Ghôr, and a mile wide. It is thickly overgrown, and is called "the jungle [pride] of the Jordan" (Jeremiah 49:19). The Jordan itself is normally only a very small river, twenty-five or fifty feet wide, within the Zôr. When, in flood, it overflows, it spreads over the Zôr.

Near Jericho is the spot Joshua had chosen to make his crossing into Canaan. The priests bearing the Ark of the Covenant were to walk through the waters, and the men were to follow about a half-mile behind. As soon as the feet of the priests came "to the brink of the waters," God dammed up the waters above that place, and they passed through dry-shod.

Some have explained this as "a miracle of coincidence," and others claim that it is an absolute miracle apart from any coincidence. Who knows? I can tell you what the coincidence might be, although I

---

[1] Nelson Glueck, in his fascinating book, *The River Jordan* (Philadelphia: The Westminster Press, 1946), 268 pp., calls it "Earth's Most Storied River." For good photographs showing the Ghôr and the Zôr, see Figs. 2 and 4 in Glueck (pronounced "Glick").

personally am not so much inclined to that view. Less than twenty miles above the point of crossing, at what is today ed-Damiya or what in Joshua's day was called Adam, there are clay or marl banks along the Zôr. They must run fifty or a hundred feet high, and occasionally they are undermined by the water cutting away at them, and they topple over into the river. In A.D. 1267, when the Mohammedans were trying to build a bridge across the Jordan and found themselves unable to do it, they awoke one morning to discover that the river had been dammed up by an earth fall, and they hastily erected the bridge in the sixteen hours that the river's flow was stopped. In 1927, during an earthquake, the waters of the Jordan were stopped off for twenty-one hours by the falling of those mud walls.[2] There are some who believe that God, through an earthquake, through purely secondary causes, dammed up the waters at this moment by the falling of the clay walls upstream. Well, either way, at the particular moment when these people began to cross the Jordan, they were able to go through just as they had been able to go through the Red Sea. And they entered into the land.

First there was the conquest of Jericho, followed by a series of rapid conquests of the strategic cities. But let us examine the details of the story. After crossing the river, Joshua set up a base of operations at Gilgal. With his supplies across the Jordan in the rear, safe from attack, and by the constant feeding of those supplies, his whole problem of logistics was brilliantly worked out. Jericho stood in his way, guarding the roads up into the mountainous region of Canaan. Before he could capture Canaan, he must reduce Jericho. The story is told for us in the sixth chapter of Joshua. The main point to notice is the fact that the Lord gave them the city (verse 16), which resulted in thorough destruction by sword and by fire.[3]

Moving up the two valleys from Jericho, aiming at the central part of the country, Joshua conquered Ai and Bethel, moved on and took over the cities of the south, and then marched north and took the cities

[2] Cf. *Westminster Dictionary of the Bible* (Philadelphia: The Westminster Press, 1944), article on "Jordan," p. 328.

[3] Sir John Garstang excavated Jericho in the early 1930's and has "confirmed" the Biblical account. However, Miss Kathleen Kenyon has reopened the matter, with her excavations at Jericho since 1952, and has apparently invalidated some of Garstang's claims. At present, the entire matter is being restudied. Cf. K. M. Kenyon, *Digging Up Jericho* (London: Ernest Benn, 1957), 272 pp., especially pp. 256-265.

there. If you study the time references in the record, you will find that all of this took place within five years at the most. It was excellent strategy.

The mopping-up operations and the consolidation of the country took a lot longer. As a matter of fact, Joshua did not live to see it finished; it was not until David's day that the country was really unified. But Joshua's sudden invasion and quick striking at the strategic cities made it possible to take over the rest of the country at leisure. You can read the account in Joshua 6, 8, 10, and 11.

He divided the land, as Moses had told him to do, among the Twelve Tribes, so that they could settle down and take it over and make it their own. That is described in the fourteenth through the nineteenth chapters. The Levites had no land inheritance. They were not supposed to be an earthly people—they were the *spiritual* leaders of people—so they were to have forty-eight cities, four in each of the twelve tribes' apportionment. Six "cities of refuge" were set up for those who were guilty of killing—that is, not murderers, but those who involuntarily or voluntarily were guilty of *manslaughter*—that they might be spared for a fair trial (Joshua 20-21).

The organization of the land was only basic for it was not yet a unified land. The twelve tribes, through a long and bitter experience, had to be brought into a sense of unity, and finally, under the leadership of David, welded into a Kingdom. Joshua gave them only the basic organization. This done he gathered them together at Shechem (Joshua 24), and made his farewell address. And then he died at the age of 110.

Now, let us go back and pull together some of these facts, in order to evaluate Joshua. In his role as religious and military leader, the strong faith of Joshua is obvious again and again. Take, for example, the way that he captured Jericho: only a man of faith would attempt to take a city that way, to have the priests go up and march around it once a day for seven days and seven times on the seventh day, fully believing that when the people were shouting on the seventh day the city would fall. You may say "That is no way to fight a war! The whole thing is utterly ridiculous." But in the very fact that it is ridiculous we find the main lesson: it was written to prove that *the Israelites did not take that city; God took it for them!* To say that they set up a harmonic rhythm by their marching around the city, and that by marching seven days they got the ground trembling in such a way that it shook the walls down, is nonsense. You might do that on a small bridge; you could never do it on solid land. To say that with the sudden shout of the people at the end of that period of time, the sound waves went up and hit the walls and knocked the walls down is also nonsense. God was not trying to prove how smart these people were; God was trying to show them that *He* was going to take the city.

Nevertheless, as you go through the life of Joshua you will find that he used very good strategy. He was blessed by God with a military sense that is remarkable. I read some years ago that, in one of the war colleges of the world, the campaigns of Joshua are studied along with the campaigns of other great military leaders. They are recognized as sound military strategy. I am not saying this to glorify Joshua. I am pointing out, however, that God used a man with that type of genius at that particular moment in history.

Joshua established his base of operations at Gilgal, which was centrally located. It was protected from any attack from the rear; the enemy could not get at it, because the Jordan lay behind it. It was supplied by the rest of the tribes who were still over on the other side of the Jordan, where they could get plenty of foodstuffs and plenty of supplies, bring them down, get them over to the base of operations and then move them up the two valleys from Jericho to wherever the army was operating. Joshua took the center of the land first, cut the country in two, and then took each separated area. Everything about it is beautiful military strategy, however you look at it, and you realize that here was a great man in his own right, and a man who was great because of his faith in the Lord.

To say all these things about Joshua is not to overlook the fact that he made mistakes. There were at least three errors in his work and if it had not been for these the country might have been consolidated much sooner.

In the first place, Joshua was tricked into a treaty with the Gibeonites (chapter 9). The record says explicitly that he did not even wait to find out what the will of the Lord was; he entered into the treaty, and as a long-term result, the country remained disunited until the days of David. The Gibeonites, you remember, came in with their clothes in rags and their shoes worn out and their bread moldy, and they said, "We have come from a very far country . . . come; now make a covenant [treaty] with us" (9:9-11). They got him to promise that he would not destroy them as he had been destroying the rest of the Canaanites. Then Joshua found out that their city was only three days away! Because of his word he could do nothing but let them stay there.[4]

Then, he allowed the Jebusites to hold Jerusalem (Joshua 15:63) the results of which plagued the tribes until David captured Jebus.

Perhaps worst of all, Joshua failed to dispossess the Philistines, as God had commanded.[5]

As a result, Judah and Simeon at the south of the country were isolated from the other tribes in the north. The country was divided across the middle by the area of Gibeon, by the city of Jebus or Jerusalem, and by the wedge occupied by the Philistines in the hill country and the Shephelah, that portion of the country that tapers down to the sea, southwest from Jerusalem. The effects of that division were never overcome. David was able to weld the tribes together, but after Solomon's time the country split apart again forming two kingdoms, north and south, and the split was right along that old line of division!

Do you look upon Joshua as a cruel man? When he took a city, he would "devote" it. To "devote" a city to the Lord meant to kill every man, woman, and child and all of the cattle in it, and take the gold and silver and put it in the temple, or in the tent of the Lord. You and I have been brought up under the New Testament code of ethics; we believe in the teaching of Jesus on the use of force. Sometimes we find it difficult to go back into the days of Joshua and understand that he was doing what was normal procedure, and that he was a child of his time.

Even more than that, I think we have to look upon Joshua as a man who was under orders. God had told him to wipe out the Canaanites, for two reasons. First, the Canaanites deserved to be punished because of their own gross sin. We know a number of facts about the Canaanites, from the discoveries of archaeology. They were one of the most grossly depraved people of ancient history. They continued to practice child sacrifice for centuries after it had been abolished in Egypt and Mesopotamia; they made their own children "to pass through the fires of Molech"—which meant burning them alive as a

---

[4] According to our way of thinking, Joshua was not obliged to keep his word, since the Gibeonites had entered into the contract fraudulently.

[5] Dawson Trotman, in a chapel address at Fuller Theological Seminary, pointed out another grave weakness in Joshua's career: he failed to train a successor!

burnt offering. Even worse was their sex perversion. They believed that they could worship their gods, their "baalim," by entering into sexual orgies in the name of religion.[6] God wanted that wiped out. He saw that if that were allowed to continue, it would ultimately destroy the people who took over that land.

He also wanted it wiped out, I think, for another reason. We have already pointed out that the land of Canaan was the center of the "X" that you drew on the map of that time, and that the influences of Canaan went out to the whole world. The religion of Canaan could not help but have its effect abroad, and it did have its effect upon the religions of Asia Minor and Egypt, Greece and Rome. God wanted this place to be a place of testimony to a holy God by a people who were holy because they served a holy God. It was preventive surgery. God saw here a cancer at the heart of the world, and He wanted it cut out no matter what the cost. The greatest charge, I think, that we could lay at the feet of Joshua and those who were associated with him in the conquest of the country was that they failed to carry out the will of God in that respect. All of the difficulties that came later in the religion of Israel—their worship on high places, their own introduction of the glorification of sex, their Baal worship—came from the Canaanites who were allowed to stay even though God had commanded that they be wiped out.

Joshua was not so great as Moses. Is it then anticlimax to study this man after we have studied Moses? I would say no, and I would call your attention to Joshua 1:1-2: "Moses my servant is dead: now therefore arise, go over this Jordan, you and all this people . . . [and] I will be with you." God expects each generation to get up on its own feet and face its own problems. God does not want us to stand around saying, "Well, now, look at Moses. *There* was a great man! We will never have another man like Moses!" And a thousand, two thousand, three thousand years later we are still looking back and saying, "Oh, what a wonderful man Moses was; there never has been another like him." Moses is dead. Great man that he was, he's dead. Get up and face the problems of your day and your age! Arise, go over this Jordan. Don't long for the past. Do the work of the present, and God says, "I will be with you." In Joshua 4:14 we read, "On that day the Lord exalted Joshua in the sight of all Israel." He gave Joshua stature commensurate with the responsibility. He will do the same for us.

[6] For the full picture, see W. F. Albright, *Archaeology and the Religion of Israel* (Baltimore: Johns Hopkins Press, 1942; 2d ed., 1953) Chap. III.

CHAPTER VIII

Ruth

MOST OF THE outstanding characters of the Bible, for one reason or another, seem to be men; only occasionally do you find a woman among them. Such selectivity makes the few even more outstanding; the very fact that a woman's name or record appears puts a special mark on her. One of the most outstanding of these women is Ruth.

Her record—and her little Book—begins with the words: "In the days when the judges ruled. . . ." That was a period in the history of Israel which seems best characterized by the word "disorganization." Young Israel was growing up. Israel had been a young child in Egypt, under the tutelage of a foreign governor. There was no leader in Israel; even Moses, whom God did indeed raise up, was destined to be not a governor, but rather a deliverer who was to free them from bondage. When they entered Canaan, in the days of Joshua, there was still no central organization; they were twelve tribes living on twelve assigned portions of the land, and that was about all. It is summed up in the statement that "In those days there was no king in Israel; every man did what was right in his own eyes" (Judges 17:6). The emphasis you place on that depends largely upon your own philosophy: to me it means that they were doing mostly what was not right in the eyes of God. The story of Israel is the reiterated story of apostasy, repentance and coming back to God, of the Lord sending a deliverer—and of a return to apostasy, as soon as the crisis is over.

In this period lies the story of Ruth; it shines out all the more brightly because of the darkness of the period in general. The story is divided into four scenes—I have often thought it would dramatize very beautifully—and the four scenes fit very nicely into the four chapters that comprise the book. In chapter one is the beautiful story of Elimelech, his wife Naomi, their sons Mahlon and Chilion, and the wives of the sons, Ruth and Orpah.

"In the days when the Judges ruled there was a famine in the land, and a certain man of Bethlehem in Judah went to sojourn in the coun-

try of Moab . . ." (1:1). Bethlehem Judah is about five miles south
of Jerusalem, on the ridge of the land. Moab lies to the east on the other
side of the Jordan Valley at the point where the Jordan River empties
into the Dead Sea. The hills of Moab are clearly visible against a
sparkling blue sky as you look across the intervening hills of the
Judean wilderness, and from certain high points you can see the Dead
Sea lying down there, 1292 feet below sea level. Elimelech went to
Moab because there was a famine in his own land and he heard that
there was food in the land on the other side.

We are told very little about his family: just their names and little
else. The two boys, when they got to Moab, took Moabite wives. They
lived there about ten years and then the husband of Naomi died, and
not long after the sons of Naomi died. That left Naomi and her two
daughters-in-law, Orpah and Ruth. It seems as though the story is
almost ended before it has begun!

They decide to go back to Bethlehem; at least, Naomi decides that.
It is her home; it is where her relatives would be; it is where her heart
is, where her religion is. Quite commonly, in those days, people
thought of their gods geographically. When they lived in one land
they thought in terms of the god of that land, and when they moved
to another land they thought of the god of *that* land. This is probably
what Naomi meant in verse 15, when she said, "See, your sister-in-law
has gone back to her people and to her gods." I suppose that was
part of the decision in Naomi's mind—that she was going back to the
land of Jehovah.

The girls say they will go along with her. Considering the economic
and social system of the day, there was very little choice for young girls
like Ruth and Orpah, who had become widowed young in life.
Daughters were bought and sold as furniture or cattle or corn were
sold. Once they had been "purchased" by one man, they were not very
valuable in the eyes of another; frequently the widow would degenerate
into a woman of the street. These girls wanted to go along with their
mother-in-law hoping, I suppose, that someone would come their way
to save them from such a life. But Naomi does not know what to do
with them; she tells them to go to their homes (in Moab) and stay
there. And they say, "No, we will return with you." Naomi asks,
"Why will you go with me? Do I yet have sons in my womb that
they may become your husbands?" (1:11). Even if she were to get
married again that very night and have sons, would these daughters-

in-law be willing to wait around for twenty years or so, until the sons grew up to marry them?

What Naomi is talking about, of course, is the institution of levirate marriage.[1] When a man died leaving a wife with no children, his brother was obligated to marry and to raise up children not to himself but to the dead brother. We find provision for such levirate marriage in the Mosaic law (Deuteronomy 25:5-10), as well as in the cuneiform tablets.[2] Naomi was talking about that custom.

Orpah saw the futility of the situation, and decided that she might just as well go back home.

But Ruth refused to leave Naomi. In one of the most poignant statements in all literature she said, "Entreat me not to leave you or to return from following you; for where you go I will go, and where you lodge I will lodge; your people shall be my people, and your God my God; where you die I will die, and there will I be buried. May the Lord do so to me and more also if even death parts me from you" (1:16-17). There is an intensely beautiful loyalty to her mother-in-law and to the family into which she had entered by marrying the son of Naomi.

So the two of them, Naomi and Ruth, come to Bethlehem. And when they enter the city gates, you can hear the women of the city saying, "Is *this* Naomi? It doesn't look like her. How she has aged! How poor she has become!" She had lost her husband and her sons, and of course the bitter experiences had left their mark upon her. To the amazed group of women Naomi says, "Do not call me Naomi [which means 'pleasant']; call me Mara [which means 'bitter']. . . ." When she had been born, her parents had given her the name "Naomi," because, I suppose, they thought she would grow up to be a pleasant little girl and a pleasant woman with a nice personality. Now she says, in effect, "That's all gone; I'm bitter now, because the Lord has dealt very bitterly with me." So she begins her life anew.

The second chapter introduces Boaz. He was a kinsman, perhaps a cousin, of Naomi's husband, a man of wealth, of the family of Elimelech.

In the first chapter of the Book of Matthew, where Matthew gives the genealogy of the Lord Jesus Christ (verse 5) we read that "Salmon

---

[1] Cf. art. "Marriage, Levirate," in *Unger's Bible Dictionary* (Chicago: The Moody Press, 1957), pp. 700-701.

[2] Cf. C. H. Gordon, *art. cit., Biblical Archaeologist* 3 (1940):10.

[became] the father of Boaz by Rahab, and Boaz the father of Obed by Ruth, and Obed the father of Jesse, and Jesse the father of David the king." The line of Jesus develops from that. Boaz was the son of Salmon by Rahab. Now there is admittedly some question as to whether this is the same Rahab that we find in the Book of Joshua. However, I do not see why her name would ever have been brought into the genealogy if she is not the well-known Rahab,[3] for Matthew lists very few women in his genealogy; those he lists must have been well known.

Let us go back to the story of Rahab, for just a minute. When Joshua and the Israelites had encamped at Gilgal after they crossed over the Jordan, the first city in their path was the city of Jericho. It had to be conquered before they could go on the rest of the way. Joshua sent two spies on ahead to find out what the situation was in Jericho and how they could get past that city to take the country beyond it. The two spies spent the night in the house of a harlot[4] whose name was Rahab. Rahab had heard about the Israelites. She knew that they served the Lord, and she knew something of the Lord's mighty works; so Rahab made them swear that they would deal kindly with her and with her father's house, and save alive her father, her mother, her brothers, her sisters and all who belonged to them. They entered into that compact with her. And they kept it. After the city of Jericho was captured, after the walls had fallen and the Israelites had moved in, they were commanded by Joshua to burn the city and to destroy everyone except Rahab (Joshua 6:22). In Hebrews, where we have the list of the great people of the faith, it is written that by faith Rahab the harlot was saved out of the destruction of Jericho (Hebrews 11:31).

If this is the same Rahab—and to my mind it is, although there is always the possibility of two persons with the same name—then Boaz

---

[3] A comparison of the genealogy given in Ruth 4:18 with that in Exodus 6:14-25 may be helpful in this connection. Since Aaron had married Elisheba, the daughter of Amminadab the sister of Nashon, and since Amminadab and Nashon are the immediate ancestors of Salmon and Boaz, we have an indication that Salmon belonged to the generation after Aaron (Salmon's father Nashon was Aaron's brother-in-law). The capture of Jericho certainly occurred in the generation after Aaron, and, according to Matthew 1:5, Salmon married Rahab, and their son was Boaz.

[4] According to some scholars the Hebrew word had come to mean something like "inn-keeper." This view is at least as old as Josephus (A.D. 90). But I see little reason to try to explain away the obvious moral standards of that day.

was her son. At any rate, he was the child of faith, for we find gleaming from him this vital faith in the Lord.

Ruth went to Naomi one day and said, "Let me go to the field and glean among the ears of grain after him in whose sight I shall find favor" (Ruth 2:2). According to the law of Moses, anyone was allowed to take from a field of grain as much as he could eat on the spot or as much as he could pick up after the reapers had passed. Moreover, the reaper was told that for the sake of the poor he should not cut the *corners* of the field; he should leave a little grain standing there so the poor could get it. It was a humanitarian provision of the law of God,[5] to take care of the poor of the land. Ruth was planning to go into one of the fields and get enough grain to feed Naomi and herself.

She went, and she happened to come to that part of the field belonging to Boaz (verse 3). It just "happened"—I do not believe she planned it that way. But actually, things do not "just happen" in this world. God has His hands in things; all things work together for good to them who fear God, and who try to follow His will. Ruth came to the field of Boaz, and as she was working there with the reapers, she gathered up the little bit in the corners to take home.

Boaz came from Bethlehem. He greeted the reapers with the words, "The Lord be with you"; and they answered, "The Lord bless you." He looked them over, and apparently he knew who were working for him, for he asked, "Who is this young girl?" Bethlehem was not a large city; it just had a few hundred people—too small, according to the prophet, to be listed among the thousands of Judah. All Bethlehem knew how Naomi had gone out to Moab and how she had come back with no one but her daughter-in-law. So they told Boaz, "It is the Moabite maiden; and she asked us to let her glean and gather among the sheaves, and she has been here from early morning till now, without even stopping for a rest."

Can you not hear Boaz say to Ruth, "Now listen; don't go to glean in any other field; you stay right here in mine. Stay close to my maidens. I have charged[6] the young men in this field not to molest you.

---

[5] Like many other elements which God led His people to preserve, this was pre-Israelite. The *kashka* in the Nuzu tablets seems to have been a portion left in the field when reaping. Cf. E. A. Speiser, "New Kirkuk Documents Relating to Security Transactions," *Journal of the American Oriental Society,* 52 (1932): 362 ff.

[6] This is an interesting verse for the study of the use of verb tenses in Hebrew. Actually, Boaz had not yet given such a command; he had only just ascertained the facts. But when an action is determined, it can be expressed "as good as done" by the past tense.

When you are thirsty, go to the water-jars and drink what the young men have drawn." In amazement and modesty she bows her face to the ground and says, "Why have I found such favor in your eyes, that you should notice me?" And Boaz says, "Well, I've heard about you. I've heard what you have done for your mother-in-law since the death of your husband, how you left your father and your mother and your native land and came to a people that you never knew before. The Lord bless you; the Lord recompense you for what you have done, and may a full reward be given you by the Lord God of Israel under whose wings you have come to take refuge!"

We like Boaz when we first meet him because he is a man with a vital religious experience. The Lord is not just a name on his lips; the Lord is a Person whom he serves, and to whom he looks for blessing and for reward.

Ruth worked until the evening, beating out what she had gleaned, and she had about an ephah of barley—about a bushel—and she took it home and showed it to her mother-in-law. Naomi asked, "Where did you glean today?" Ruth told her: "In the fields of a man named Boaz." Naomi said, "Blessed be he by the Lord, whose kindness has not forsaken the living or the dead! . . . The man is a relative of ours, one of our nearest kin" (2:19-20).

The "near kinsman" is another idea that we have to get clearly in mind to understand the story. Beside the rule of levirate marriage, which said that a man should marry his departed brother's wife and raise up children to his brother, there was also the law of the near kinsman which said in effect that in the case of a widow who had no one that she could claim in levirate marriage, the nearest male relative was under obligation to consider seriously marrying the young widow in order that she might have a place to live. It is hard for us to picture these things, because today, if a woman is left without a husband early in life, there might be some insurance to help her for a few years. She can probably find work. There is no stigma attached to her remarrying. But in Ruth's day, she could not be independent. She could not go out and get a job. She could be "redeemed"[7] by a near kinsman, or she could enter into a life of prostitution. That was about the only choice she had. Boaz was the near kinsman, and Naomi advised Ruth to stay close to him and see what would develop.

Chapter three of the Book of Ruth is the third scene in this drama—

[7] The verb "to redeem" is used to form the word (*gō'ēl*) used for the "near kinsman." Often *gō'ēl* is translated "redeemer."

and by suggesting that it is a drama, I do not mean to imply that it is unhistorical. It is quite historical; but it is dramatically told, isn't it? Naomi decides that the situation needs a little pushing, and she takes it upon herself to see if she cannot do *something* about getting this young man who is a near kinsman to marry her daughter-in-law. She says, "My daughter, should I not seek a home for you, that it may be well with you? Now this Boaz, who owns the field where you are working—is he not our kinsman? See, he is winnowing barley tonight at the threshing floor" (3:1-2, paraphrased). And she tells Ruth to wash and anoint herself and put on her best clothes and go down to the threshing floor and find out where Boaz is going to sleep. When he has eaten and has had his wine for the evening and lies down to sleep, she is to crawl in at his feet.

I suppose this sounds a bit *risqué;* no respectable young lady would do that today, would she? A mother would hardly advise her daughter today to use this method of getting a man; but under the customs of ancient time, there was no reproach. We do not find Boaz reproaching this young girl; as a matter of fact, he feels rather flattered that she has not thrown her life to the young men in the field, but that she has come to him.[8]

When he had eaten and drunk, and his heart was merry, he went to lie down at the end of a heap of grain, and she came and uncovered his feet and lay down. About midnight he awoke with a start and behold "a woman lay at his feet!" He said, "Who are you?" and she answered, "I am Ruth, your maidservant; spread your skirt over your maidservant for you are next of kin" (3:9).

But, he was *not* next of kin. I do not believe *Ruth* knew that; I am not even sure that *Naomi* knew it. But *Boaz* knew it. It would seem that he had already considered his responsibility to this young girl, because he had uncovered the fact that there was another man in Bethlehem who was more closely related to her than he, and that other person must be given the right of first refusal.

So he tells Ruth that ". . . you have made this last kindness greater than the first . . . do not fear, I will do all that you ask, because [according to the Hebrew] the gate knows that you are a virtuous

---

[8] From time to time, I have heard an objection expressed to reading such portions of the Bible. This displays, in my opinion, a false sense of morals. After all, if God chose to include such stories in His Holy Scriptures, who art thou, O man, to criticize? These things must be understood in the light of their day. To this we might add, "Honi soit qui mal y pense."

woman." The gate is the place in the city where everything happens, where all of the gossip is passed, where all town business is transacted, where all the letters are written. Boaz says, ". . . now it is true that I am a near kinsman, yet there is a kinsman nearer than I. Remain this night and in the morning, if he will do the part of the next of kin for you, well; let him do it; but if he is not willing . . . I will do the part of the next of kin for you" (3:12-13). She stays until it is early morning. Before it is light enough to recognize anyone, Boaz sends her home; but first he fills her mantle with grain so that if anyone should see her, they would think she had gone out early in the morning to get some grain. She goes home and tells Naomi all about it.

Chapter four is the conclusion of the story; the scene is laid at the city gate. Boaz goes up to the gate and sits down; everybody has to go through that gate sooner or later during the day, so at last along comes the next of kin. We are not even told his name. Boaz collects some of the elders who are sitting around the gate—I have seen them in the East many times, the old men sitting there by the city gate; they have nothing else to do! They are supported by the younger men of the family. The word for "old man" and the word for "witness" are the same in the Babylonian language. The witnesses are the old men who sit by the gate. Boaz gets ten of these together and he says, "Sit down; you are my witnesses." Then he says to the next of kin, "Naomi who has come back from the country of Moab, is selling the parcel of land which belonged to our kinsman Elimelech. So I thought I would tell you of it and say, 'Buy it in the presence of those sitting here, in the presence of the elders of my people.' If you will redeem it, redeem it; if not, tell me, because there is no one beside you to redeem it, and I come after you." And the nearer relative says, "I will redeem it." Ah, but there is a little catch, a condition that must be met. Ruth is involved; the kinsman will have to take her with the land, in order to "restore the name of the dead." The kinsman objects. He had not thought of that, and what is more, he cannot afford it.

Why could he not afford it? Well, it was a matter of protecting his estate. Under the law, the minute he took Ruth and married her, he contracted to raise up her children not to himself, but to her dead husband! These children immediately became a drain on his resources; furthermore, they threatened the inheritance of his own children: those who were not his own children to carry on his line would threaten the inheritance of the children who were. It is too much; the next of kin backs off, saying, "I cannot redeem it [the land] for myself, lest I impair my own inheritance. Take my right of redemption yourself . . ." (4:6). Boaz must have chuckled; that was the way he wanted it!

Then they do a strange thing—at least it is strange to us. The next of kin takes off one sandal and hands it to Boaz. That seals the bargain. Boaz turns to the elders and the people standing around, and says: "'You are witnesses this day that I have bought from the hand of Naomi all that belonged to Elimelech and all that belonged to Chilion and to Mahlon. Also Ruth the Moabitess, the widow of Mahlon, I have bought to be my wife, to perpetuate the name of the dead in his inheritance, that the name of the dead may not be cut off from among his brethren and from the gate of his native place; you are witnesses this day.' Then all the people who were at the gate, and the elders said, 'We are witnesses. May the Lord make the woman, who is coming into your house, like Rachel and Leah, who together built up the house of Israel'" (4:9-11).

So Boaz took Ruth as his wife. Out of the marriage came Obed, the grandfather of David. Notice that it is Naomi who brings up the child (4:16). This act, apparently a form of adoption, put the child in the legal family genealogy, for it was Naomi who had the right to hand down the succession. She was the one, you remember, who had title to the field. Ruth, after all, was an outlander and a stranger; she would have no genealogical authority. If Naomi had not taken the child and adopted him as her very own, the line of heritage would have been broken.

It is a beautiful story, and it has a beautiful lesson which, as I see it, is this: *The ordinary event of everyday life becomes an important step in God's redemptive plan.* Just suppose Ruth had not gone to the field of Boaz. Suppose Boaz had not felt compelled to go through with the responsibility which was laid upon him as a redeeming kinsman. Or suppose Ruth had not had enough faith to go back home with Naomi; or that Naomi had not had enough faith to take her along. Can you see how God's plan would have been thwarted?

I am not suggesting that you and I, by doing some of the commonplace things of everyday life, can be the means whereby a saviour comes into the world. Our Saviour has already come. But the commonplace things of life are the means whereby God does some of the most

RUTH # RUTH 87

important things He has to do. We never know, when one of these little ordinary events comes along, what the results may be. We can bring about unknown and untold good just by faithfulness in the commonplace things of every day.

CHAPTER IX

Samuel

THE PROPHET Samuel has been called the last and greatest of the judges and the first of the prophets. Many Jewish writers look upon him as the first great prophet after Moses. It was Samuel who, under God, had the responsibility of setting up the kingdom and anointing their first kings.

The period *before* the time of Samuel was a rather chaotic time in the history of Israel.[1] They had come out of the land of Egypt a subjected people who had never been responsible for handling their own affairs. For generations they had been slaves, and one of the advantages (if it *is* an advantage) of being a slave is that you do not have to plan for yourself. Everything is planned for you. You do what you are told to do, you get what you are given, and that is all there is to it. But that does not build a nation; neither does it develop independence.

In Canaan, God's promise to Abraham was to be fulfilled: the Israelites were to become a great nation and they were to have many blessings from God. But they were a disorganized people; they were twelve tribes, with intertribal jealousy and strife, and on one occasion one of the tribes was almost wiped out in an internecine quarrel. In those days, "every man did that which was right in his own eyes," and that which was right in his own eyes was not always right in the eyes of God. So God gave them judges, and those judges appeared at critical junctures in the history of the Israelites to lead them a little more steadily in the way that God intended.

Samuel was the last of the judges. Immediately preceding him was Eli; I think the best way to begin the study of Samuel is to begin with a study of Eli.

Eli was judge and his sons were priests in the land. According to I Samuel 2:12, the sons of Eli were worthless men. They had no regard for the Lord. They violated the custom and insisted upon a better

[1] For an interesting description of these days, see Werner Keller, *The Bible as History*, pp. 169-182.

share of the offerings. "They had treated the offering of the Lord with contempt."

Eli was not blind to the faults of his sons. It must have been a bitter experience in the life of this old man, who had been judging Israel for about forty years, to discover that his sons were so unworthy. In verse 22, we read that "Eli was very old, and he heard all that his sons were doing to all Israel, and how they lay with the women who served at the entrance to the tent of meeting. And he said to them, 'Why do you do such things? For I hear of your evil dealings from all the people. No, my sons; it is no good report that I hear the people of the Lord spreading abroad. If a man sins against a man, God will mediate for him; but if a man sins against the Lord, who can intercede for him?' But they would not listen to the voice of their father. . . ."

The time came when God had to reject this old man and his sons and tell him that although He has previously made a promise (back in the days of Moses and Aaron) that the family of Eli would be the one to continue the priesthood; yet, because of the sons' infidelity and worthlessness, God was going to break that agreement. A man of God came to Eli and told him in a cryptic way that he, Eli, would live to see the sudden death of his two sons on one day, and that his own heart would be consumed with the grief of it (2:28-31).

The punishment came about in an interesting way—quite an ordinary way, you might say. Chapter 4 tells us about it. Israel went out to battle against the Philistines; Israel was encamped at Ebenezer and the Philistines at Aphek. The battle was going against Israel, and someone got an idea: "Why don't we send for the Ark of the Covenant?" The Ark they had carried through the wilderness; it had been in the Tabernacle, representing the presence of God Himself between the cherubim; it had been carried by the priests across the Jordan so that the water dried up and they could walk dry-shod. Why not bring the Ark into battle now, so that the Lord Himself would be there? What an immature concept they had of the presence of God! If only they could get God on the battlefield they would win! So, without stopping to ask if this were the Lord's will or not, they brought the precious Ark into the battle.

But the Lord was displeased because they had not sought His will. Graphically the story is told: "A man of Benjamin ran from the battle line, and came to Shiloh the same day, with his clothes rent and earth upon his head." Eli was sitting by the side of the road watching;

he was troubled because they had taken the Ark of God down to battle without finding out the Lord's will, and he asked for news. "How did it go, my son?" The Benjamite said, "Israel has fled before the Philistines, and there has been a great slaughter among the people; your two sons also, Hophni and Phinehas, are dead, and the ark of God has been captured" (4:12-17).

The words fell upon Eli like the blows of a hammer. It was bad enough that his two sons had been killed in the battle, but when he learned that the Ark had been captured, the old man, who was sitting on a stool, fell over backward and broke his neck and died.

It was in Eli's day that Samuel was born; it was in the latter years of his judgeship that Samuel grew up, and began to fulfill the duties of the priestly office. Go back to the first chapter of I Samuel and read the account of the birth of Samuel. His father was Elkanah, of the tribe of Benjamin of Ephraim, and he had two wives: Hannah and Peninnah; Hannah had no children. Elkanah used to go up to Shiloh every year to sacrifice to the Lord of hosts—this was a century before the building of the temple at Jerusalem. There he would give portions of the sacrifices to Peninnah his wife. He loved his other wife, Hannah, but he would only give her one portion because the Lord had closed her womb.[2] That used to irritate Hannah. She would weep about it. Finally she went and prayed to the Lord and made a vow: "O Lord of hosts, if thou wilt indeed look on the affliction of thy maidservant, and remember me, and not forget thy maidservant, but wilt give to thy maidservant a son, then I will give him to the Lord all the days of his life, and no razor shall touch his head" (I Samuel 1:11). In other words, Samuel would be under the Nazirite vow.[3] If she could only *have* a son, Hannah was in effect saying, she would not even ask to keep him. The fact that she *had* a son would satisfy her.

The Lord heard her prayer and the son was born in due time; and when he was weaned (which among the Hebrews would be some time in the second year), she took him, together with an offering of a three-year-old bull, a ephah of flour, and a skin of wine, and brought them

[2] The verse is difficult. Others interpret it to mean that Elkanah gave Hannah a double portion. Verse 6 is also difficult to interpret: who was irritated by whom, Hannah or Peninnah? I understand it to mean that Hannah was irritated by the presence (and possibly jibes) of her husband's other wife; others interpret it to mean that Peninnah was irritated by the displays of love for Hannah by Elkanah.

[3] On the Nazirite vow, see *Westminster Dictionary of the Bible,* art. "Nazirite," p. 421.

to the house of the Lord at Shiloh, where she made her offering: "For this child I prayed; and the Lord has granted me my petition which I made to him. Therefore I have lent him to the Lord; as long as he lives, he is lent to the Lord" (1:27-28). So far as we can tell from the rest of the story, she never took the child home again. He stayed there at Shiloh and Eli in the temple and grew up in the service of the Lord.

There is another beautiful little touch in the second chapter, which tells of how his mother used to make him a little robe each year and take it to him in the temple. As the child grew, his clothing, as you mothers know, did not grow with him. So Hannah would take a larger size the next year and give him the robe as she offered the yearly sacrifice. And Eli blessed Elkanah and his wife and said, "The Lord give you children by this woman for the loan which she has lent to the Lord" (2:20). Her reward is told in the twenty-first verse: ". . . the Lord visited Hannah, and she conceived and bore three sons and two daughters. And the boy Samuel grew in the presence of the Lord."

Here then is a child who had come out of a godly home, the child of a very devout mother who was willing, if she could only have a son, to turn him over as soon as possible to the Lord's service.

The next high point in the story is the call of Samuel. He was ministering to the Lord under Eli. We do not know how old he was at this time, nor are we told how old Eli was. I suppose Samuel was in his early teens, or even younger. We are told in 3:1 that the word of the Lord was "rare" in those days. The people were living in a time when it seemed as though the heavens were shut away from them. Eli's eyesight had begun to grow dim, and he could not see; he was lying down in his place; the lamp of God had not yet quite gone out. Samuel was lying down inside the temple where the Ark of God was.

And the Lord said, "Samuel, Samuel!" And he said, "Here I am . . ."; and he ran in to Eli. Do you see how natural all of these things are? You and I do not live under the experience of those days, when God would pick out one particular person and speak to him or speak through him; we live in the dispensation of the Holy Spirit when God speaks to us by the Spirit, chiefly through His Word. But in those days it was not so. I believe that this child, who had not been through the experience before, actually heard a voice calling him by name, and went into the next room and said to Eli, "Here I am; you called me." Eli replied, "I did not call you; lie down again."

He went back and lay down and the voice came again saying, "Samuel!" And he went to Eli again and said, ". . . you called me"; and Eli denied it again. We are told that Samuel did not yet know the Lord, and that the word of the Lord had not yet been revealed to him.

Then the Lord called Samuel a third time, and he went into Eli and said, "Here I am; you called me." Eli at last perceived that the Lord was calling the boy, and he said, "Go, lie down, and if he calls you, you shall say, 'Speak, Lord, for thy servant hears.' " And he went back and lay down; and God came to him and spoke to him, and told him what was going to happen—that he was going to fulfill against Eli the things that He had spoken concerning Eli's house from the beginning to end, and that He would punish him because his sons were blaspheming God and he did not restrain them.

We cannot help but stop a moment at a verse like this to point out that there is an element of responsibility which falls upon us as parents. Eli, although he certainly could not be blamed for what his sons were doing, was blamed because he made no attempt to restrain them. He apparently was letting them go their own way. We read once of a more or less half-hearted effort to stop them, but apparently they were too far gone by that time.

It was soon after this that the Spirit of the Lord came upon Samuel, and (verse 20) "all Israel from Dan to Beersheba—from the city farthest north to the city farthest south—knew that Samuel was established as a prophet of the Lord."

This is a different situation from that which existed in the days of Eli's judgeship, when there was no frequent Word of God. Samuel becomes the means by which God can speak to His people, and it seems as though God has come back again to His land, at Shiloh, while Samuel is dwelling there.

The next step in the study of Samuel is the study of his connection with King Saul. Samuel was trying to organize the people into some kind of unity. They were still twelve tribes; still going their separate ways. One of the tribes had had an abortive effort at kingship with Abimelech, but we can scarcely refer to Abimelech as the first king of Israel. Samuel "went on a circuit year by year to Bethel, Gilgal, and Mizpah" (7:16). If you look at those places on a map, you will see that they are in the central part of the land of Canaan, lying almost in a circle. It would seem as though Samuel was making this annual tour to try to hold the people together.

The nations around them had kings, and the nations around them, especially the Philistines, were attacking the Israelites from time to time. The elders of Israel on one occasion gathered with Samuel at Ramah and said to him, "Behold, you are old and your sons do not walk in your ways; now appoint for us a king to govern us like all the nations" (8:5).

Some of our modern historians tell us that the reason why Samuel was reluctant to give the people a king was because he was an old meddler, a manipulator, and that he wanted the kingship for himself. I don't believe it! I think he was an idealist, and that he felt that to put a king over this people would be to increase their problems. He pointed out what would happen if they had a king: "These will be the ways of the king who will reign over you: he will take your sons and appoint them to his chariots to be his horsemen, and to run before his chariots; and he will appoint for himself commanders of thousands and commanders of fifties, and some to plow his ground and to reap his harvest, and to make his implements of war. . . . He will take your daughters to be perfumers and cooks and bakers. He will take the best of your fields and vineyards and olive orchards and give them to his servants. He will take the tenth of your grain and your vineyards and give it to his officers. . . . He will take your menservants and maidservants, and the best of your cattle and your asses, and put them to his work. He will take the tenth of your flocks, and you shall be his slaves" (8:11-17). Perhaps the picture was a bit overdrawn, but it is still true. When you get government, you must pay for government. In our day, we would say that "all this means increased taxation!" Samuel was saying that to his people. But they wanted a king, and God told Samuel to go ahead and give them a king.

Now this is one of the points that is often contested in Old Testament study: whether or not it was God's will that there should be a king. It *was* God's will that there should be a kingdom. He had spoken about it before this. To have a kingdom, you have to have a king; therefore, God would have given these people a king in due time, when it was His will that it should happen. I think that the sin here lies not in the desire for a king but in the fact that the people were running before God. They were crying for a king before God had chosen to give them one, and therefore the king they got turned out to be pretty much of a failure. He was not a king after God's own heart. Another had to be sent to replace him.

We come now to Saul, who was the son of Kish and a man of the tribe of Benjamin. The asses of Kish were lost and the young man and a servant were sent out to hunt for them. They covered quite a bit of ground as they hunted; they went through Ephraim, through Shalisha, through Shaalim, and through the land of Benjamin. When they came to Zuph, Saul said, "Come, let us go back, lest my father cease to care about the asses and become anxious about us." But the servant said, "There is a man of God in this city, and he is a man held in honor; all that he says comes true. Let us go there; perhaps he can tell us [where the asses are]" (I Samuel 9:5-6, slightly paraphrased).

So they went up into the city and asked if the seer were there. (Samuel was known as a "seer" at this point, not as a "prophet.") Samuel had been told by the Lord, "Tomorrow about this time I will send you a man from the land of Benjamin, and you shall anoint him to be prince over my people Israel. He shall save my people from the hands of the Philistines" (9:16). As Saul and his servant drew near, Samuel heard the voice of the Lord saying, "Here is the man of whom I spoke to you!" Saul approached Samuel and asked, "Where is the house of the seer?" Samuel answered, "I am the seer; go up before me to the high place, for today you shall eat with me, and in the morning I will let you go. . . . As for your asses that were lost three days ago, do not set your mind on them, for they have been found" (9:19-20).

Saul realized, by this time, that he was in the presence of a man who knew a lot more about what was happening than he did; meekly, he followed Samuel. As they sat down to eat, Samuel said to the cook, "Bring the portion I gave you, of which I said to you, 'Put it aside.'" When he gave Saul the choice cut of the meat Saul wondered what it was all about. Why should he be treated like this? He found out why the next day: on the outskirts of the city, Samuel told him to send his servant on ahead, so that they might be alone. There Saul knelt while Samuel poured oil on his head and rose the first king of Israel.

But something more was necessary to make the kingship complete: Saul needed the approval of the people he was to rule. Samuel took care of that, too. He called the tribes together and said in effect: "You want a king. Let's make it legal; elect a man from one of your tribes!" They did just that; they cast lots and selected the tribe of Benjamin as the one from which their king should come; from the tribe of Benjamin, the family of Kish was picked as the family from which he would come; and from that family, the choice fell on Saul. What a choice! He stood head and shoulders above any man in sight; he was handsome, courageous, looking every inch a king. Saul was just what they needed. And all the people shouted, "Long live the king!"

But even that was not enough to make Saul king. Some asked, "What's he king *of*?" Others, "He's good looking, but what will he do when a war comes?" It was not long before they found out: war with the Ammonites came, as told in chapter eleven, and Saul met the acid test; he led his people to victory over the people of Ammon. At last he was really king! He had been anointed by the prophet, chosen by lot by the people, and established as a military hero by winning a great battle. He had the goodwill of the people, the courage of a true king, the face of a god. No finer candidate for the throne could have been found in Israel—at least so it would seem.

The next person in the life of Samuel is David. There is not much to tell of David in this connection, for the Bethlehem youth was still young when Samuel died; there is just enough to round out the picture. In I Samuel 12, the old prophet called upon his people to witness to his honor and honesty; he called upon them to say whether he had ever taken anything from them fraudulently, or in oppression. They swore that he had not. Then he told them of *their* record; he reminded them of their sinfulness and disobedience and called upon them to repent. He promised that "if you still do wickedly, you shall be swept away, both you and your king" (12:25). They went on doing wickedly—both people and king.

Saul got into a battle with the Amalekites; he had previously been told by the Lord to wipe them out to the last man and the last animal. But he disobeyed; he saved some of the best animals and he allowed Agag, king of the Amalekites, to get away alive. Samuel came to Saul after the battle, heard the lowing of oxen taken alive from the enemy, and discovered the rest of Saul's disobedience. The word of the Lord came to Samuel: "I repent that I have made Saul king" (15:10).

Repent? *God* repents? How could He? I think God is speaking here in words and speech that the people can understand. It was not God's will that Saul be made king; God had, humanly speaking, given in to the wishes of the people. So, still speaking in human terms, God says, "I repent that I have made Saul king; for he has turned back from following me, and has not performed my commandments" (15:11). Samuel was angry and he cried to the Lord all night. After all, Samuel was in this thing too; he had gotten himself mixed up in a nice mess, anointing this man as king. He did not want his reputation marred for doing that; he did not want to be repudiated, either, by the people of God. He felt, at first, that he must defend Saul; to turn against him would be to admit that he was wrong. But when he heard the lowing of the oxen and discovered the king of the enemy alive, he knew in his heart that he had anointed the wrong man: *Saul never should have been made king.*

Samuel faces Saul in a dramatic scene, with a dramatic accusation: "Though you are little in your own eyes, are you not the head of the tribes of Israel? The Lord anointed you king over Israel, and the Lord sent you on a mission, and said, 'Go, utterly destroy the sinners, the Amalekites, and fight against them until they are consumed.' Why then did you not obey the voice of the Lord? Why did you swoop down on the spoil, and do what was evil in the sight of the Lord?" (15:17-19). Saul offers his poor excuses: he *did* obey, really; he captured the king; he took just a *little* of the spoil; it was the *people* who took most of it! But Samuel is not impressed; he pronounces the doom of an outraged God upon the house of Saul, and then grieves over Saul. At last, after the Lord has chided him for the delay, he turns to find a successor, David. He anoints David, then returns to his house at Ramah. In a simple, immortal statement the Scripture records his death: "Now Samuel died; and all Israel assembled and mourned for him, and they buried him in his house at Ramah" (25:1).

The greatness of Samuel has to be measured against the times in which he lived. It was a chaotic period in Israel's history; those were the formative years. We have a parallel in the colonial days in America, before we were "the United States," in the days when we were more divided than united, and not yet pulling together. Israel was divided twelve ways, as the colonies were divided into thirteen. At the head of Israel stood Saul, beset with a terrible melancholia that at times seemed madness; no man's life was safe in his household or his court. Division in the state, insanity at court: in the midst of this stood Samuel, a lonely figure of tremendous stature, a man whose job it was to start the organization of a kingdom. He did not live to see that kingdom in its days of glory, under David and Solomon; his was only to prepare Israel for her days of glory.

There were many obstacles. The people turned on him, demanding a king. He gave them their king. But Saul proved to be unworthy of the throne and not a man of God, for the simple reason that he was chosen on the human basis of appearance and human courage, and not on the basis of spirituality or devotion to God. Through all of this, Samuel stood firmly—the one great character of the whole affair. He was the man through whom God could work His will. Eli falls, Saul falls, David is still a shepherd boy—but there stands Samuel!

There is something magnificent in being God's man in difficult times. It is not as glamorous as being God's man in the days when things are going well. But—suppose there had been no Samuel? Suppose there had been no one to hold things together, no one to guide, or counsel, or rebuke, or point out God's way? Would the kingdom then have come into existence? Perhaps so; perhaps God would have raised up someone else—but the fact remains that He raised up *Samuel,* the last of the judges and the first of the prophets, and laid great work upon him in full confidence that he would do it, and do it well. And Samuel did it well; no man can deny that.

CHAPTER X

David: The Man

DAVID is considered by many to be the greatest character in the Old Testament after Moses. I suppose, when we start talking about which one is "greatest," it is a matter of personal choice and preference, and there are many factors that enter into our decision. Each of the characters that we have been studying has some particular characteristic, some particular value, that makes him worth studying. Joshua was blessed, for example, in that he had the opportunity of leading the people into the land which God had promised Abraham; David was blessed in that he had the privilege of setting up the kingdom in that land.

God brings us back repeatedly to situations in which we can see the continuity of His whole program: the promise to Abraham is not something we study and forget; it recurs in the lives of most of these Old Testament figures. The same thing is true when we get into the New Testament; we find there that we are not starting with a whole new series of persons, but each one has some particular part in that unfolding plan of God by which He accomplishes His eternal purpose.

David was the one who set up the dynasty. Saul, of course, had been the first king of Israel, but Saul did not set up the eternal dynasty; it is not "the house of Saul," but "the house of David" which is forever. The house of David does not lack a man to sit on the throne of the kingdom: David's greater son, Jesus Christ, is of the house and lineage of David, not of Saul. So, you see, in a particular way David is the one who in God's wisdom and in God's will brought about, here on earth, in its initial stages at least, the kingdom of God which God had foretold when He made His promises to Abraham.

David's story starts in the sixteenth chapter of I Samuel, and runs through the rest of the First Book of Samuel. He was born in Bethlehem. Jesus, you will remember, was also born in Bethlehem, because He was of the house and lineage of David. Bethlehem is "the city of David."

We gather that David had a godly mother. There are, I think, two references to that in the Psalms: in the 86th and 116th Psalms, both of which are ascribed to David. In Psalm 86:16 he prays to God, "Turn to me and take pity on me; give thy strength to thy servant, and save the son of thy handmaid." Likewise in Psalm 116:16 he refers to himself as "the son of thy handmaid." We may be reading too much into it, but it is nevertheless true that David referred to his mother as "the handmaid of the Lord," at least twice in the Psalms, and the inference from that statement is substantiated by the life of David, in which we find the characteristics of a man who has been brought up by his mother to know the Lord and to trust Him.

Of course, there is a lot more to a religious life than just that. David goes through some other experiences in which he seems to lose his faith or in which it weakens or wavers, and he has still other experiences in which his faith seems to come back with a new strength. His Psalms indicate that he had passed through many such experiences. But the fact remains—we shall see it brought out over and over again in these studies—that the early training that a child has from his parents, and particularly his mother, is extremely important. We cannot overemphasize that lesson. It is one of the truths the church must insist upon in its teaching, and Christians must accept and believe and act upon.

David is described, in I Samuel 16:12, as "a ruddy lad, with beautiful eyes and handsome." Later on in life, he got into some strange situations because of his attractiveness; women ran after him, singing, "Saul has killed his thousands, but David his ten thousands," and it started a chain reaction of jealousy in the mind of Saul that led to a great deal of difficulty. David was a fine looking young man. Tradition has it that the word "ruddy" here implies that he had blue eyes and a fair complexion with blond or reddish hair.

Of course, you know that David was a shepherd. He is described in I Samuel 16:11 as keeping the sheep while the rest of the family of Jesse were at home; further on, he describes himself to Saul by saying, "Your servant used to keep sheep for his father, and when there came a lion or a bear and took a lamb from the flock, I went after him and smote him and delivered it out of his mouth; and if he arose against me, I caught him by his beard and smote him and killed him. Your servant has killed both lions and bears" (17:34-35). Some think that he is boasting, but I rather imagine there is a factual basis for it; I doubt that he was saying this to impress Saul because, after all, he was in a situation where to impress Saul was to put himself up against the giant Goliath, and there was no need for him to stick his neck out *that* far!

His bravery is emphasized again in the contest with Goliath. The Philistines were one of the thorns in the side of the Israelite kingdom in the days of Saul and in the early days of David. They lived down on the seacoast, fifty to sixty miles southwest of Jerusalem, and they extended their territory in a sort of wedge pointed northeast toward the Israelite kingdom, specifically toward Jerusalem. The wedge increased in size as the strength of the Philistines increased, and decreased whenever the Israelites grew strong. The frontier was fluid; whenever the Philistines became overstrong, they would extend their lines and stretch into Israelite territory and take more of the country; and the country in that area, we might add, is the best country in the whole land of Palestine for grape vineyards, olive orchards, and the general raising of crops.

Now the Philistines were engaged in one of those conflicts when someone got a good idea: "Why bother having a full-scale war, when we can settle it with a combat between just two men?[1] Let us pick out one of our men, and let the Israelites pick out one of theirs, and let the two of them slug it out; whichever man is victor, we'll say his side won. It will save us all a lot of trouble." That *is* a smart way to conduct a war, particularly if you happen to have a giant on your side. And the Philistines had a giant named Goliath of Gath. His height was six cubits and a span. A cubit is the length of your forearm from the point of your elbow to the tip of your long finger, usually around eighteen inches. A span is, of course, the length which you span with your fingers between the outstetched thumb and the end of the small finger—about eight inches. So a man six cubits and a span in height, would be somewhere in the neighborhood of nine feet eight inches—not an unreasonable height for a giant. Some think that this is one of the fairy tales from the days of giant killers, and they point out that there are no such giants now. But nine feet is not an incredible height for a human being; giants of the present day are known to exceed eight feet. Two years ago, if I am not mistaken, there was a basketball team in this country that could put on the floor at one time an entire team, every man above seven feet in height. So you see this is not an unreasonable story.

[1] This use of the single combat is found also in Homer's *Iliad*.

Goliath's head was covered with a helmet of bronze. He wore a coat of mail that weighed five thousand shekels of bronze—about 125 pounds. His legs were protected below the knees with greaves (thin plates) of bronze. Slung across his shoulders was a javelin of bronze, and in his hand was a spear that had a shaft like a weaver's beam and a spearhead that weighed six hundred shekels of iron—about fifteen pounds.[2] In addition to this, he had a shield-bearer who went before him. You see, Goliath had very little chance of losing when he suggested, "I'll go out there and I'll fight any representative of Israel, and whoever wins the battle will be the victor."

The Israelites took one look at him and decided it was a rather difficult assignment. They held off for days, and he taunted them. He shouted over to them, "Why have you come out to draw up for battle? Am I not a Philistine, and are you not servants of Saul? Choose a man for yourselves, and let him come down to me. If he is able to fight with me and kill me, then we will be your servants; but if I prevail against him and kill him, then you shall be our servants and serve us. . . . I defy the ranks of Israel this day; give me a man, that we may fight together" (I Samuel 17:8-10). The Israelites were dismayed. They looked around; they could find no one willing to enter into the unequal battle—until David came along and offered his services.

The story in the seventeenth chapter suggests that this had been going on for some time; there was a daily taunting by the Philistine giant, and Israel was doing nothing about it. Then David comes, looks at the situation and says immediately that he will go in and battle him. Saul says to him, "You are not able to go against this Philistine to fight with him; for you are but a youth and he has been a man of war from his youth." David replies, "The Lord who delivered me from the paw of the lion and from the paw of the bear will deliver me from the hand of this Philistine." Saul felt that if David insisted upon going into this thing, he had better be protected, and so he clothed him with his own coat of mail, and put a helmet of bronze on his head. David put on his sword, over his armor; he tried hard, but he simply could

---

[2] The shekel, we know from actual weights that have been recovered, varied considerably: some shekels are 2½ times as heavy as others from different places and times. I am using the value 1 shekel equals 0.4 ounce, which, in my opinion, is reasonable here. For a study of weights and measures, see G. A. Barrois, "Chronology, Metrology, etc.," in *The Interpreter's Bible* (New York and Nashville: Abingdon-Cokesbury Press, 1952ff.), Vol. I, pp. 142-164.

not use that sword, nor wear the armor. He said, "I cannot go . . . I'm not used to them."

Do you see the fix he is in? He is a young man who has been accustomed to living in the open as a shepherd with his flocks; he was probably so fleet-footed that he could race around to one side of the flock when he saw a little lamb straying off that direction, and get back to the other side quickly if he saw danger coming there. Now he is weighted down with much more than the little cloth mantle that he would wear while he was out with the flocks, and he is unable to maneuver. He takes off the armor, drops the sword, and arms himself with the weapon he knows best.

He takes his staff in his hand; it is something like a club. He chooses five smooth stones from the brook; puts them in his shepherd's bag, and takes his sling in his hand. You can still buy those slings; I bought one in the market place in Bethlehem. It is a knit affair, with two long strings coming out on each side, perhaps a foot or fifteen inches long. The center of it is woven into an almost circular shape, two or three inches across. The idea is to put a stone in the center and whirl it around several times and then let go of one end of it. The stone will travel much farther than you could throw it, because you get so much velocity at the end of the sling. In the hand of a practiced slinger it is a lethal weapon.

The Philistine came down and looked at this boy and when he saw him he said, "Am I a dog, that you come to me with sticks?" And he "cursed David by his gods." Then he taunted David, saying, "Come to me, and I will give your flesh to the birds of the air and to the beasts of the field." But David said, "You come to me with a sword and with a spear and with a javelin; but I come to you in the name of the Lord of hosts, the God of the armies of Israel, whom you have defied. This day the Lord will deliver you into my hand, and I will strike you down, and cut off your head; and I will give the dead bodies of the host of the Philistines this day to the birds of the air and to the wild beasts of the earth; that all the earth may know that the Lord saves not with sword and spear; for the battle is the Lord's and he will give you into our hands" (17:43-47).

Notice that the confidence of this young lad is not in himself; his confidence is in the Lord. He feels that the Philistines have dared to defy not only Israel; they have defied also the Lord of Israel. And David takes one of the stones and lets it go and catches Goliath in the forehead, and Goliath sinks to the ground; and while he lies stunned on the ground David runs over, takes his sword, and cuts off his head—and that is the end of Goliath.

That put the Philistines to rout, and it put David immediately in the eye of the people. As a result he came into Saul's court. There are two accounts in the Book of Samuel of how he got into the court;[8] I rather imagine both of them are true, for Saul was psychologically the kind of man who would do something and later on forget that he had done it. He probably brought David into his court and then forgot that he had him there. Lonely, the boy went back home with his father and the flocks. Later he came to the attention of the king a second time, in the conflict with Goliath, and the king asked, "Who *is* this fellow?" And he took David back into his court.

Another of David's characteristics was his musical ability. He was able to play on the harp—well, it is called a harp in our English Bibles, but actually it was a lyre.[4] The music was, I suppose, similar to what I have heard played by some of the Oriental musicians along the streets of their villages—a rather haunting kind of music. Not many of us today would have any fondness for that particular type of music, but after you have heard it for a while, after you have lived with it for two or three months, you get used to it, and there is a haunting delightfulness about it. It seems to have had therapeutic value for Saul in his moments of madness, for he would call David in and David would play this music. It "drove away the evil spirit in Saul" and helped him to compose himself. But gradually this evil in the mind of Saul built up until he became so completely jealous of David that it was impossible for David to stay there. He was forced to leave the court.

David had formed a friendship, really a deep devotion, with Jonathan, the son of Saul. It is all the more remarkable, I think, because Jonathan had come to know that Saul had been rejected by the Lord and that David would ultimately take over the throne which should, by the line of blood, go to him. Even so, he warned David of what was going

[8] The first account is told in I Samuel 16:14-23. The matter is further complicated by II Samuel 21:19, where we are told that it was Elhanan who slew Goliath. But I Chronicles 20:5 says that Elhanan slew the brother of Goliath. This is not the place to try to solve this knotty problem.

[4] For an archaeological indication of what this lyre looked like, see Fig. 76 (p. 123) in G. E. Wright, *Biblical Archaeology* (Philadelphia: Westminster Press, 1957).

on in the mind of Saul, and finally he helped David get away from Saul and find refuge in the outlying territory.

This brings us to the second period of David's life, his outlaw existence. Sometimes, when I have called David an outlaw, I have been rebuked for it. I have been told that this really is not the right word to use about a Bible character. But it is exactly what David had become. He lived off the country, by marauding and plundering; at one time he had to save his life by taking the shewbread, the bread of the presence, from the altar of the Lord. Jesus referred to that when He was rebuked by the Pharisees for breaking the Sabbath, pointing out that even David, when the circumstances required, had to go beyond what was legal to maintain his own life. The young man became not only an outlaw with reference to the laws of King Saul, but a violator of the written law of the Scriptures, in order to stay alive.

Then David accepted protection from King Achish, a Philistine king who had been an enemy of his country. If you read the story in chapter 21:1-9, you find that David seems to have lost much of his faith in the Lord. He went over to the enemy—*almost*. But he got hold of himself in time and by feigning madness he was able to get away from King Achish. Then he came to the cave of Adullam (chapter 22), where he went through an experience which I think is reflected in some of the Psalms. Psalm 34, for example, seems to contain the story of his regaining the faith: "This poor man cried, and the Lord heard him, and saved him out of all of his troubles." The Psalm goes on to say, "O taste and see that the Lord is good!" Some of the other Psalms reflect the same story.

David next gathered around himself a group of outlaws like himself, men who were not acceptable to the government of Saul. With them he succeeded in protecting the borderland of Israel against the forces of the Philistines, so that even though he and his men were not under King Saul, they were actually working in the King's interests. On two occasions at least, perhaps on three occasions, Saul went after David. David had the opportunity to kill him, but he restrained himself. He had by that time learned to depend on the Lord, not on himself. Psalm 57, I think, reflects that story. The heading of Psalm 57 is "To the choirmaster: according to Do Not Destroy.[5] A Miktam[6] of David,

---

[5] Possibly indicating that this Psalm is to be sung to a familiar vintage tune. Cf. Isaiah 65:8.

[6] An obscure Hebrew word, perhaps another musical notation.

when he fled from Saul, in the cave." In that Psalm David tells the story of how he cried to God and how he found his refuge in God; how he lay in the midst of lions that greedily devour the sons of men. He could say, "My heart is steadfast, O God, my heart is steadfast!" He did not seek to deliver himself; he was perfectly content to let God work this thing out in *His* own time. He refused on several occasions to do anything whatever to hasten the day when he should take over the throne from Saul.

We bring our story to a close with the reference to the Philistine war, which is told in the last few chapters of I Samuel and the death of Saul which is described in the first chapter of II Samuel. You might think this event would bring joy to the heart of young David because now he could say, "Well, Saul is out of the way; at last I can take over the throne." Instead, you find sincere mourning. Saul was God's man, although Saul had turned against God. David realized that you cannot stretch out your hand against the Lord's anointed. Then, too, Jonathan, Saul's son, had been David's best friend. The news that Saul and Jonathan had been killed broke the heart of David.

Just to study this much of his life, without going into the great events of his kingdom (which we will do in our next chapter) is to see something of the character of this man. He had gone through all sorts of adversity, all sorts of persecution; he had even wandered away from the faith which he had at the beginning, into a mild sort of unbelief. He had sought to live by his own wits, rather than by trust in God; and then in a rich, deep, spiritual experience he was brought to trust in God and to see how much God would do for him. He was willing to sit back and wait until God's time came for him to take over the kingdom. He refused to move on his own, or do anything to get rid of Saul. That was his character! We shall see even more of it as we see how he leads the nation step by step. We shall see something of the other side of his character, too, when we discover that he is a man who has sinned deeply. He knows it and his Psalms reflect it.

CHAPTER XI

David: The King

IN THE WORLD of sport we often hear the expression "color." While I cannot exactly define it, I think you understand what it is; the athlete with "color" makes his easy plays look spectacular and his mistakes are readily forgotten. The batting champion goes down swinging like a windmill, the all-American tackle fails to throw a block, the heavyweight contender leaves himself wide open—and still we love them, if they have color. Bad manners on the field are overlooked. We love them just the way they are.

David had color. I think it is for this reason the Bible can portray him in what some writers call "an honest story." The curtain is never drawn before certain episodes in his life. He stands there in full gaze, warrior or weakling, saint or sinner. We know all about David. And we love him. We have already followed the early days of his career, down to the death of Saul. In this chapter, we shall study David the King. But we shall not lose sight of David the Man—for he is the same person. His weaknesses may seem more obvious, his sins more glaring, his victories more thrilling, now that he is king. Even his name seems to take on new significance. If the evidence of the Mari tablets has been rightly interpreted, *dawîdûm* was a title, perhaps like "generalissimo,"[1] but to students of the Bible, David will always mean "beloved."

After the death of Saul, David located his capital at Hebron, in the south of the land of Palestine. Actually, he was king only of the southern part of the land known later as Judah. There was a tendency toward a division into north and south throughout the history of Israel. Only for a little while was it really united. It was one kingdom during the latter portion of David's reign and the early reign of Solomon. Then it broke apart again.

The continuing house of Saul, which had not been killed off (David

[1] G. Dossin, "Benjamites dans les textes de Mari," in *Mélanges syriens offerts à M. René Dussaud*, Vol. II (1939), p. 981.

did not follow the practice of wiping out the whole house) tried to establish a ruling dynasty in the north. For seven years David ruled in the south while the rival kingdom held forth in the north.

The first four chapters of II Samuel record the end of the house of Saul and the complete victory of David. The end came largely through the treachery of Abner, Commander of Saul's army.[2] After that, David was king over the entire country.

One of the first things that he did as king was to conquer the stronghold of the Jebusites, the city of Jebus, which we know better as Jerusalem. One advantage of Jebus was that it was centrally located, at least more centrally located than Hebron, which was twenty miles farther south. Moreover, it was neutral territory, never having been held by the south or by the north. It was in the hands of the Jebusites until it was taken by David; therefore there was no emotional tie to either north or south, hence no entering wedge that might tend to divide the kingdom again. The southerners could not say, "The capital is in *our* part of the kingdom," nor could the northerners say, "No, it is in *ours*." It was on neutral ground. Somewhat the same principle led the founding fathers of our nation to locate our capital in the District of Columbia rather than in one of the states.

The capture of Jebus is described in the fifth chapter of II Samuel. The arrogant Jebusites said that "the lame and the blind" could keep Israel from taking the city. They had reason to be arrogant: the city stood high on its hills, the valley of Kedron on one side and the Tyropoean Valley on the other; and it was well fortified. No one in the days of Joshua or since had been able to take it. David, however, did the seemingly impossible. The description of his strategy has been a puzzle until recent years. Some thought David's army went through the city water-course; but now it seems that they used hooks and scaling ropes to go up over the walls.[3]

The archaeology of Jerusalem has been somewhat discouraging, and as a result the picture is not yet too clear. Let me say briefly that it now appears that someone in the second century B.C., perhaps Simon,

[2] It is perhaps worth a passing note to observe that such military *coups* have always been an unstabilizing force in the Middle East, and the present day is no exception.

[3] This is discussed by W. F. Albright in "The Old Testament and Archaeology," *Old Testament Commentary,* H. C. Alleman and E. E. Flack, eds. (Philadelphia: Muhlenberg Press, 1948), p. 149. The older viewpoint has been maintained, however, in several more recent works by other authors.

as reported by Josephus, levelled the ground and dumped all previous remains into the valley.[4] But it seems certain from studying that dump that David's city was located on the southeastern side of the present-day city, overlooking the pool of Siloam. When you visit Jerusalem, they will show you the hill of Zion on the southwestern side of the old city, overlooking the valley of Hinnom. In fact, I have visited "David's tomb" there. This appears now to be certainly wrong.

David's city, you may be surprised to learn, was not large: about twelve hundred feet long and four hundred feet wide, it was only about as long as two modern city blocks and narrower than one—about eight acres. But it was a very important city and once it was taken, once it was made the capital, it became extremely important for all of the rest of the history of Israel.

David then proceeded to conquer the neighboring states. The first one he went after was that of the Philistines, because in the days of Saul they had repeatedly attacked the southwestern boundaries of the land. He defeated them so thoroughly that they never again were a serious threat to Israel, and then turned his attention to the east, to the states on the opposite side of the Jordan. He subdued the Ammonites and the Moabites, the Edomites and Amalekites, and I do not know how many others. It called for war and David went to war although he was not, strictly speaking, a man of war. He seems to me to have been, on the whole, a man of peace. But in order to establish and secure his kingdom, it was necessary for him to put down these various peoples who were disturbing the peace of the land. It is one of the ironies of history that David, who by nature would have been a peaceful man, was refused the privilege of building the temple because he had "shed much blood" (cf. I Chronicles 22:8).

Then he turned his attention to the organization of the kingdom. The organization of David's kingdom, which is described largely in I Chronicles 22-27, is very interesting. It gives us a good insight into the mind of the man. He apparently realized that the kingdom was not to be built on the personality of the king alone, but on an organization of men around him. He seems to have taken many of his ideas from the Egyptians, but whether he got them directly, or through his knowledge of the Philistines (you remember that in the days when he was an outlaw he had lived with the Philistines), we do not know. The organizational structure of his kingdom was a sort of pyramid. It had

[4] For a fuller description, see G. E. Wright, *Biblical Archaeology*, p. 126.

a broad base and narrowed toward the top, where there was just one man as king.

At the base were a number of mercenaries, or paid foreign soldiers. There was wisdom in that, because there would be no emotional tie-in on the part of these mercenaries with any particular group in the country. Above them were "The Thirty"—thirty men, although the number probably varied from time to time, chosen because of their bravery and their wisdom in leading armies. I suppose the men would be "generals" today, or perhaps, "colonels," or possibly they would be looked upon as a "cabinet." Above the thirty, "The Three"; these three would have, of course, delegated authority over the thirty. And then, at the top would be David himself. David's authority extended through this long chain of command, reaching out to the whole nation.

David also made the offices of the scribe and the recorder important and prominent in his kingdom. One of our present-day historians says that the first real historiographer was David. I suppose that statement would be challenged by many, and yet, there is truth in it. Long before the time of Herodotus or any of the other famous historians, David caused details to be recorded, and this record could be later used for the purpose of constructing an authentic history. Many of the things that we know about him and his kingdom, and many of the things that we know about the kingdom that followed the days of David, we know because David set up the office of recorder. This official was called, in Hebrew, the *mazkîr*, "the one that causes you to remember." The record was called, if we translate it literally, "The Book of the Affairs of the Days of. . . ." In other words, it was a day-book, a journal, a log-book of the important events kept day by day. We use the impressive title "Chronicles"—but "minutes" would be more meaningful. Such a record is not a history; it is the raw material from which history can be written.

You will notice, as you read through the Old Testament, frequent statements such as this: "Is it not written in the Books of the Kings of Israel and Judah?" That does not refer to the Book of Kings in the Bible; it refers to the journal, the day-book, which had been kept by the recorders in the kingdom of Israel or Judah. You also read in certain instances of kings who, when they could not sleep at night, or when they were troubled, got up and read those chronicles. They would come across the record of the work of some good man, and they would suddenly ask themselves, "What happened to that man, anyway? Was he rewarded for what he did?" The king would call in someone and ask, "Was he rewarded or not?" Perhaps it had been overlooked. That is how Mordecai happened to be honored by Ahasuerus, as we read in the Book of Esther.

In addition to introducing the *mazkîr*, which can be translated "speaker" or "chancellor" as well as "recorder," David seems to have been first to establish in Israel the office of the *sôfēr*, usually translated "scribe." This was an ancient and honorable office in Egypt. One of my favorite art objects from Egypt is the famous Scribe from Sakkara, now in the Louvre.[5] With his lifelike inlaid eyes and the color and physique of a lifeguard, he sits there ready to take dictation—and he has been sitting that way since 2500 B.C. David seems to have introduced the scribe into Israel, probably as a civic official. But we know that by the time of Jesus, the scribe had become the religious lawyer. How? By becoming first, certainly by the time of Ezra, the one charged with the copying and care of the Holy Scriptures. The modern equivalent of the *sôfēr* is the secretary. I suppose few secretaries stop to think that they belong to an honorable profession, which at one time ranked next to the king. As a matter of fact, at least two kings of ancient times boasted that they had learned to write! So, you young ladies who take dictation and punch the typewriter, lift up your heads! And just remember—even today, the highest officers in our land, beneath the President and the Vice President, are honored with the title "Secretary."

David's next move was to bring the Ark of the Covenant from Kirjath-jearim to Jerusalem. We have already mentioned that Saul had very foolishly taken the Ark into battle, and that the Philistines had captured it. However, that proved to be a blunder, for the Ark caused a great deal of trouble in the Philistine cities. It seems that no matter where they would take the Ark, the next morning they would find the idol of their Philistine god, Dagon, flat on his face on the ground. So finally they decided to get rid of the Ark. They sent it back to the Israelites. But the Israelites also moved it about from one place to another and it was never properly housed. Then, one day, "it was told King David, 'The Lord has blessed the household of Obed-edom and all that belongs to him, because of the ark of God.' So David went and brought up the ark of God from the house of Obed-edom to the City of David with rejoicing . . ." (II Samuel 6:12). A tent was made

---

[5] This statue can be seen pictured in many books on Egypt, and is particularly well presented in J. B. Pritchard, ed., *The Ancient Near East in Pictures*, Fig. 230.

to cover it and they ". . . set it in its place, inside the tent which David had pitched for it; and David offered burnt offerings and peace offerings before the Lord" (6:17).

Jerusalem thereupon became not only the political center of the kingdom, but the center of religious life as well. Forever after Jerusalem is looked upon not only as the city of kings, but as the city of God. The prophets three to five centuries later are talking about Zion as the place from which "the law of the Lord goes forth." Zion is the city to which the nations of the world and the kings of the world will come in order to worship Jehovah.

In connection with that worship, we read in I Chronicles 16 that David set up a musical system. He appointed certain of the Levites "as ministers before the ark of the Lord to invoke, to thank, and to praise the Lord, the God of Israel." Asaph was to sound the cymbals, Benaiah and Jahaziel the priests were to blow trumpets continually before the Ark, and others were to play harps and lyres. The seventh verse suggests that the first "Psalm" (cf. Psalm 105:1-15) was sung that day. A regular order was set up for this work, in order that there might be music and praise to God.

All this has been questioned by some historians in recent years. Starting from the conviction based on knowledge available to them that the development of music and of musical instruments was not older than the Greeks, they felt that the Biblical story could not be accurate. We know differently now, thanks to modern archaeology. In the Ugaritic materials, discovered at Ras Shamra since 1929, the same word for "singers" occurs (dating from the fourteenth century B.C.) as is used in the account of David, three centuries later. On the wall of the tomb at Beni-Ḥasan in Egypt a painting was discovered, dated about 1900 B.C., portraying thirty-seven Asiatics (Canaanites or Amorites) who had come to Egypt. One is carrying a lyre.[6] In the burials from the Third Dynasty of Ur, a magnificent lyre was found, which can be seen reconstructed, in the University of Pennsylvania Museum.[7] Music and musical instruments can therefore be traced back at least to 2000 B.C. in both Egypt and Mesopotamia; and we have already seen the great influence that these two cultural areas had on the land of Canaan.

[6] This can be seen in the lower register of Fig. 9, *Westminster Historical Atlas* (1945).

[7] This is reproduced in color in L. Woolley, *Ur: The First Phases* (The King Penguin Books; London: Penguin Books, 1946), plate 6.

Religious hymns were sung to the accompaniment of instruments among the Israelites as early as the time of Moses, according to Exodus 15. The elements of worship, we have seen, can be traced back to Moses and the tabernacle service. Bands of prophets in the days of Saul apparently worshiped at the "high place" with harps, tambourines, flutes, and lyres (cf. I Samuel 10:5). But it was David, according to Hebrew tradition (and there is no longer any good reason to doubt it), who was responsible for a marked development in what we might call "ritual" in the service. It was David who laid the foundations for the Book of Psalms.

Here again we must take issue with the scholars who have insisted on dating the Israelite cultural elements unduly late. No scholar, to my knowledge, has insisted that David wrote all the Psalms; and certainly no Old Testament scholar today would deny that there are "late" Psalms in the Bible—just how late, will be a matter of debate. But to deny that David is the psalmist, to deny that he, more than anyone else, is responsible for the development of this particular type of devotional literature in Israel, is sheer nonsense. Who else is there in Hebrew tradition? Certainly such a man must have left his name somewhere; and the only name that has been indelibly inscribed in tradition is the name of David. As the Law must ultimately and essentially be traced to Moses, so must the Psalms be traced to David.

David chose the Oriental king's prerogative, namely, to establish a harem. Several writers have noted that Saul had only one wife and one concubine; David, on the other hand, had a large harem, with many wives and many children. Once again, it is necessary for us to learn to judge men by the standards of their own day, rather than by the fuller light that God has given us. And once again, we must recognize that the experiences of the men and women in the past have been recorded for our benefit, so that we can see objectively the results of their moral standards. If anyone is inclined to justify polygamy on the basis that "David did it," let him weigh carefully the results that accrued to David from polygamy.

One story in particular has been preserved for us in unusual detail, and it merits our careful consideration: the story of David and Bathsheba. It is told in II Samuel 11.

Late one afternoon, David arose from the midday nap that is characteristic of life in the Middle East, and he went up on the roof of his house for a walk in the fresh air. He saw a woman bathing; and the woman, the Bible tells us, was very beautiful. David's sensual nature was aroused, and he inquired about the woman and discovered that she was the wife of one of the Hittite soldiers in his army. So David sent for her, and "she came to him, and he lay with her" (11:4).

In his book, *A History of Israel,* T. H. Robinson makes the astute observation that it would have been considered quite normal and natural, quite within his rights, for an Oriental king to take the wife of one of his subjects. It is to be looked upon as an indication of the high view of human rights in Israel that the king felt obliged to try to cover up his act.[8] Accordingly when David received the news from Bathsheba, "I am with child," he attempted to shift the blame. He called Bathsheba's husband home from battle, and tried to persuade him to take some of his "accrued leave." Uriah refused to sleep with his wife during the time of war. The taboo upon the marriage relation in time of war seems to have been rather widely observed in the Ancient Middle East. We even find it mentioned in the Dead Sea "War Scroll." Next, David wined and dined Uriah until he was drunk (verse 13); but still Uriah did not go to his own bedroom. Finally, David in desperation, sent Uriah back to war, and at the same time issued an order to Joab the commanding general, "Set Uriah in the forefront of the hardest fighting, and then draw back from him, that he may be struck down, and die" (verse 15). You can call that anything you want, but to send a man into the hottest part of the battle and then pull back all of the other troops so that he is left there alone—that is *calculated* murder. Uriah was killed, and after a "respectable" time for the weeping and the mourning period, Bathsheba was married to David.

Now when we talk about David, we say, "Here is a man after God's own heart." But some one will ask, "How can you say, 'Here is a man after God's own heart,' when he did things like that?"

Well, we have to keep two things in mind here, one of which is that God looks upon us, *not according to what we do, but according to the sincere faith in our hearts.* David was a man of God's own heart, even if he was a sinner. You say then, "Well, if God excused all of his faults, then we can go out and do anything we want and claim that we love God, and God will overlook it." Not at all! Go back and read the record again, and see what happened. David was punished *for everything he did.* As a matter of fact, David's entire life seems to change

---

[8] Theodore H. Robinson, *A History of Israel* (Oxford: Clarendon Press, 1932), Vol. I, p. 225.

from this moment on; the world would say, "His luck changed; from that day on, it was all bad."

Shortly after his affair with Bathsheba, David saw his home disrupted, first of all by the rape of his daughter, Tamar (13:1); then by the death of the son of Bathsheba, who was born out of this adulterous union (12:15); then by the revolt of his beloved son, Absalom (15:17), and then by the death of Absalom (18:14). Down to his dying day, David was haunted by the ghosts of his sins, for his house was divided by jealousies and schisms, his favorite wife Bathsheba was plotting an intrigue to put her son Solomon on the throne, and his sons were instigating a revolt which even involved the religious leaders. The "house of David" may have been permanently established, but certainly his home was shattered several ways.

Read through the Psalms and see the grief of this man and how his heart was torn, and you will realize that God does not let a man get away with *any* sin. I remember an illustration of this, which I heard many years ago. A father was trying to teach a boy something about the principle of forgiveness, and the boy got the idea that he could get away with wrongdoing. So the father took a board, a beautiful piece of wood that had been nicely finished, and he drove some big nails into it, and then he pulled the nails out: there were scars left in the wood. And there were scars left on David's heart; the scars were there all through his life. To read the Book of Psalms and to look at the history of David's life is to realize that he was torn and twisted all through life as the result of his own sin and his own selfishness. That is one part of the story that we *must* remember.

The other part, the greater truth—and we have a Christian church and Christian ministers proclaiming the Christian gospel only because it is true—is that God *does* forgive sin. David paid for his sin, yes. He also had his sins forgiven. You and I have our sins forgiven. God does not hold these things against us forever. Sin brings its own penalty, for the penalty of sin is built into our physical and psychological nature. But sin also has its forgiveness. God is a God of love and of redemption.

If God should measure sin, who could stand? Which of us, who so readily condemn David for what he did, would have any greater claim on the love of God? But God does not deal with us that way. The message of Calvary, the message of the New Testament, the message of the whole Bible from beginning to end, is the message of a God who deals with us, not according to the sins we commit, but in His redeeming love. If our hearts are turned toward Him, if we have a longing to live above sin, if our hearts are filled with the sincere desire to follow God, then God for Christ's sake will pardon us. The story of David and his life tells us that. The story of Jesus Christ and His death on Calvary also tells us that.

CHAPTER XII

Solomon

SOLOMON has been referred to as the wisest man who ever lived. The "wisdom of Solomon" is proverbial—and I am convinced that it is based on factual foundation; for as in the case of Moses and the Law and in the case of David and the Psalms, it is necessary for anyone who denies the tradition to put forth a more likely candidate. Who else is there? Solomon is the only man known who could have been the fountainhead of Hebrew wisdom literature.

Solomon has also been referred to as "a great son of a greater father." I rather like that description, for it tells in a few words the sad story of a son who never rose to the heights occupied by his father. In this chapter, as we examine the record of Solomon, we shall see why. The story of Solomon can be studied in three phases: his background, his reign, and his contribution to the religious life of his nation. Each of these phases, in my opinion, proves disappointing.

Some of my students get the impression, when I am teaching about the Solomonic era, that I am a bit of a "de-bunker." For some reason, Sunday school teachers and preachers have been overanxious to present the best side of Biblical characters and play down the other. At least, that has been my experience. And then, when we start to read and think for ourselves, we find that the Biblical characters are human beings like ourselves: they have feet of clay. The reaction sometimes is tragic. It is my firm conviction that we have nothing whatever to gain by altering the picture, and nothing whatever to lose by adhering to the truth. If the Bible presents a man as somewhat less than a saint, that is the best way to study him. So, with the conviction that we can learn best by seeing exactly what kind of man Solomon was, what kind of man God had to work with, and what God was able to do with and through him, we turn to the first phase, his background.

There is little more than a passing reference in the Bible to Solomon's youth. This fact in itself is odd enough to attract our attention. His mother was Bathsheba, David's favorite wife. Solomon was not the child of the sin of David and Bathsheba—that child died—but he was the next child, the fourth son born to David's wives in Jerusalem (II Samuel 5:14).

There is no evidence in Solomon's life of any early religious training. Neither is there any evidence that Bathsheba was a godly woman. At first glance this may seem strange; yet, as we think about it, does it not fit in with other details of the portrait? If she *had* been more of a godly woman, Solomon would have been more certain of the faith that was within him. There are some who feel that we have a description of Solomon's mother in the description of the godly woman in the thirty-first chapter of Proverbs. But this chapter is attributed to Lemuel; and I see no reason whatever for trying to identify Lemuel with Solomon, or for trying, on such a very doubtful basis, to construct a picture of Bathsheba from these proverbs. Her sin with David might lead some of us to the hasty conclusion that she was a completely godless woman. But let us be careful with our judgments! Her sin with David was, at least in part, David's fault. He was the king. When he ordered her to come to his house, she was in the position of a subject, and as a subject she probably had to obey. She may have been a willing subject, but at least we cannot put all of the blame on her for that episode. At most we can say that the Scripture fails to record any evidence of repentance on her part.

In the picture we have of her in the first chapter of I Kings, she seems to be pretty much of a schemer and a plotter. She arranged to have the kingship handed down to her son Solomon, rather than to the oldest son in the line of succession, Adonijah.

In addition to the fact that Solomon was the son of such a woman, he grew up in a polygamous home. David married often; the Bible records eighteen wives. We have not met a situation quite like this before—at least not so extreme a situation. Jacob, of course, did have two wives, plus the handmaid of each of those wives, in his home; and Jacob's home illustrates in small measure what David's home illustrates in large measure. The sons of Jacob were at tension, pulling against each other; and there were petty jealousies and rivalries in that home. But in David's home, where the thing was magnified all out of proportion by the large number of wives that he had in his harem, the tensions were even greater. Here were the children of all these wives fighting for position and preference. It can be established sociologically and psychologically, entirely apart from the religious viewpoint, that polygamy is not ideal, that it introduces not only the jealousy and strife of the wives in the home but the strife of the children of those wives as well. The home becomes the scene of all sorts of plots and counterplots to gain favor and to occupy places of prestige. Solomon grew up in that kind of environment.

Then, too, he grew up in the splendid days of David's kingdom. That should have been helpful to Solomon, for it is good to live in a great day. Solomon must have known that God took a small people of no significance, and brought them to a place of great importance for no other reason than that He had delighted in them and that He had *chosen* them. Solomon must have known that He had led them out of bondage of Egypt, had guided them with a strong hand through the wilderness for forty years, had fought the battles in the conquest of Canaan, had located them in the land, and at last had made them a great nation. All of that was Solomon's heritage. This boy should have grown up with a magnificent concept of the power of God—and I think he did.

But perhaps all this had certain disadvantages as well. It may have developed in him a distorted sense of the value of material things; for it seems to me that, as Solomon increased in length of reign, his emphasis upon money, wealth, and splendor increased, while his sense of the value of spiritual things diminished.

Turning to the reign of Solomon, we notice first of all that he came into the kingship through a plot. Adonijah, the son of Haggith (one of David's wives), was in line for the kingship after the death of Absalom, and Adonijah saw that David was an old man now, a bedridden invalid, unable to maintain his kingdom, just waiting for the end of life to come. So Adonijah decided that he was going to take over the throne. He prepared for himself chariots and horsemen, and he brought together Joab, who was commander-in-chief of David's army, and Abiathar, one of the priests; and this evil trio arranged to have a public demonstration in which Adonijah would be hailed as king. He very cleverly omitted to invite Solomon or Zadok the priest, or Benaiah the chief of David's bodyguard, or Nathan the prophet, or anyone else who was or who might be potentially on the side of Solomon. He was not going to let anyone come to this party who might come with the wrong kind of speech!

Word of the conspiracy got back to the prophet Nathan, and he went to Bathsheba with what amounted to a two-pronged attack to get David to act. In accordance with Nathan's suggestion, Bathsheba went in to David with a mincing speech that said, in effect, "Didn't you promise your little wife that Solomon would be the next king? And now Adonijah is calling himself king, and you aren't even paying attention to him; and he is planning a big coronation banquet, and he has invited your sons, and Abiathar the priest, and Joab the commander—everybody except Solomon! And the people are waiting to see what you are going to say. And if you don't name your successor before you die, Solomon and I will be put to death as disloyal to the new king!" Bathsheba had not even finished her speech when Nathan came in and asked, "Have you named Adonijah as your successor?" And he repeated the details of Adonijah's *coup d'état*. This stirred David into action; Solomon was officially named the next king, and plans were made for his anointing and his coronation. When Adonijah heard what had taken place, he faded into the background with his supporters. The time seemed ripe for revolt; but apparently Adonijah and his backers had no heart for revolution. So Solomon became king.

Soon after, Solomon started a building program, which is so amazing that it seems almost incredible, even in our times. First he built the temple which his father David had wanted to do, using forced labor, and enlisting the help of Hiram the king of Tyre,[1] and the Phoenician artisans who knew a lot more about handling bronze and stone and wood than the Israelites did. We get an idea of the cost of that temple from the fact that Solomon raised a levy of forced labor out of all Israel numbering thirty thousand men. He sent them to Lebanon at the rate of ten thousand a month—one month in Lebanon, two months at home, apparently without pay—for the purpose of cutting the famous "cedars of Lebanon." The cedars had to be transported from the heights of Lebanon to the sea, lashed together in rafts and floated down the coast, then transported overland to Jerusalem. Stones had to be cut at the quarry under Jerusalem, and we are told that the size of some of those stones was considerable (I Kings 5:13-18). By the time Solomon had finished, he had a temple twice as large in length and width and three times as high as the tabernacle.[2] Built of costly stone, it was overlaid

---

[1] When reading the Scriptural account, we must be careful to distinguish Hiram the King from Hiram the skilled craftsman (I Kings 5:1, 13-14). The latter is also called "Huram my father" or "Huram-abi" (II Chronicles 2:13).

[2] Although the temple was a large building for its day, it would be rather small by our standards: 90 ft. long, 30 ft. wide, and 45 ft. high, or (if we use the larger cubit) possibly about 15 per cent larger in each dimension.

with cedar so that not a stone was visible anywhere; and the interior of the holiest place was overlaid with gold on top of the cedar, and was furnished with gold cherubim and gold candlesticks. Everything was truly magnificent. Outside, in the outer court, a huge bronze altar and a bronze laver were set up. Our heads swim when we read these details, particularly when we realize that it was in the tenth century before Christ. The bronze work was cast in the Jordan valley, where there was plenty of clay, and hauled up the mountains to Jerusalem— in itself quite a feat, in view of the fact that Jerusalem is twenty-six hundred feet above sea level and the plain of the Jordan is about a thousand feet below sea level. The bronze columns ("Jachin" and "Boaz") were about 40 feet high and 6 feet in diameter, cast about 4 inches thick, with a hollow core. The bronze laver or "sea" was cast of metal of the same thickness as the columns, about 7 or 8 feet high and 15 feet in diameter, holding eighteen thousand gallons. The bronze altar was 30 feet square and 15 feet high. The skill and craftsmanship involved in making these castings is astounding, and will only be truly appreciated by those who have attempted such large castings.[3]

After Solomon built and dedicated the Lord's house, he built his own house. I think we get some idea of Solomon and of his sense of proportionate values in the seventh chapter of First Kings, where we read that he was seven years building God's house and thirteen years building his own! In other words, it was about two for Solomon to one for God. That is a pretty good way of measuring the man. He put far more time, far more money in building his own house, the Hall of the Cedars of Lebanon, the wall around the palace, and the palace for his Egyptian queen, than he did upon the building of the house of the Lord. At the same time he built stables, fortified the outposts of the nation, and spent money right and left on all sorts of "projects." Some years ago, when the New Deal was spending money, I remember that one project cost $4.8 billion. At the time it seemed to be an astronomical figure. Solomon's building projects cost about the same as

[3] The Howland-Garber model of the temple is the best reconstruction known to me. Pictures of it can be found in several publications, e.g., *Unger's Bible Dictionary*, pp. 1078-79, and a film-strip of it is available from Professor Paul L. Garber, Agnes Scott College, Decatur, Ga. I saw a full-size reproduction of the bronze sea in the new Mormon Temple in Los Angeles, but since the sanctification of the temple, this is no longer open to visitors.

that: $4.4 billion. It seems fantastic that a small kingdom should have been loaded with such a staggering cost.[4]

Down on the Gulf of Aqabah, at Ezion-geber in the southern part of his domain, Solomon had his "navy." The Israelites were never a sea-loving people, but the Phoenicians were; Solomon manned his ships with Phoenician sailors, and they sailed all over the then-known world bringing home all kinds of treasure. Once every three years they brought him cargoes of "gold, silver, ivory, apes, and peacocks" (I Kings 10:22).[5] Near Ezion-geber, at modern Tell el-Kheleifeh, Solomon built a large copper smelter. This was discovered in 1938 by Nelson Glueck and excavated during several seasons.[6] A guide, who claimed to have been Professor Glueck's guide, showed me around the remains of slag piles, blast furnaces, and workers' houses. The refinery surpasses anything known to modern discovery in the ancient world. As explained by my guide, the ore and fuel were piled in such a way as to provide flues and close contact with the heat source (probably charcoal). The blast was provided by the winds that blow almost constantly from the north.[7] Professor Albright notes that the method used for the reduction of the copper remains a mystery to specialists in metallurgy.

Solomon was a fine administrator; in this department, I think he surpassed David. He had twelve administrative districts, each one of which was required to support the court, financially, for one month of the year. When you have a harem of seven hundred wives, and three hundred concubines, and all the rest of the lavish expense at court that Solomon indulged in, you need *money!* Solomon could

---

[4] Many scholars have rejected these figures as gross exaggerations. Two facts, however, should cause us to hesitate before brushing the figures aside: Israel was in a particularly strategic position, internationally; moreover, history records the large tributes demanded of and received from Israelite kings for centuries after the Solomonic period.

[5] It was my unique good fortune to be at Eilat, the modern counterpart of Ezion-geber, in 1957, when the *Athlit* came in, the first Israeli ship since the days of Solomon to sail the Gulf of Aqabah.

[6] Glueck's description can be found in his book, *The Other Side of the Jordan* (New Haven: American Schools of Oriental Research, 1940), pp. 89-113.

[7] Modern housing in Eilat is air-conditioned by using this same phenomenon. The north side of the house is covered with a framework which is filled with desert grass over which water drips constantly. The north wind provides the breeze for an evaporator-cooler. However, two of the three days I was there, the wind was from the south (most unusual, they said!), and the cooling system was inoperative.

not very well go out and earn it, so he did the thing that politicians must always do: he had the twelve districts send in the cash. And when it came to paying off Hiram of Tyre, who was in charge of the building program, Solomon simply gave Hiram twenty cities of Galilee (I Kings 9:11-14). Already the king was selling land to finance his program. Solomon was beginning to put his kingdom in a very bad spot.

Solomon was an internationalist. In addition to his treaty with Hiram, he carried on an extensive maritime and overseas commerce (read I Kings 9—10). In the course of that commercial activity, the Queen of Sheba came to visit him. Now Sheba was a fabulous land, rich, civilized, and important to international traders.[8] The Queen brought Solomon a gift: 120 talents of gold. The talent was worth approximately $38,000—which means that the gift was worth $4,800,000. Just what it was that the Queen of Sheba wanted in exchange, we do not know; but we can have a lot of fun speculating about it. Perhaps it was a simple trade agreement.

One of the great problems of international affairs then as now was treaty-making. Treaties were made by the thousands, between big and little kings, between great kingdoms and little city-states, and for all sorts of purposes. A treaty could be made in long-drawn-out conferences and councils of state; a quicker way to do it was to arrange a marriage. Unite the king of one country with the daughter of the king in another country and presto, you had a political as well as a marriage alliance! I have no doubt that Solomon picked quite a number of his wives with one eye on political affairs and alliances. One of his wives, we know, was a daughter of the Pharaoh of Egypt: quite obviously a political marriage. I am not trying to excuse him; I am simply trying to explain how he got himself, eventually, into a sorry mess.

He did what he thought was the big-hearted, broad-minded thing, with all these wives: he allowed them to practice the rites of their own religions in his palace. He even set up places of worship outside for them, and erected idols that they might worship their own pagan gods. In the name of broad-mindedness, of good-will, of international amity and understanding, but certainly not in the name of Jehovah,

[8] The recent book by Wendell Phillips, *Qataban and Sheba* (New York: Harcourt, Brace, 1955), tells a fascinating story of explorations in the fabulous territory of Sheba.

he established this bedlam of foreign gods, and thereby set a cancer growing at the heart of his kingdom. He should have known better.

We turn now to the religious side of Solomon. When Solomon took over the kingdom, God said to him in a dream, "Ask what I shall give you." Solomon replied, "Thou hast shown great and steadfast love to thy servant David my father, because he walked before thee in faithfulness, in righteousness, and in uprightness of heart toward thee; and thou hast kept for him this great and steadfast love, and hast given him a son to sit on his throne this day. And now, O Lord my God, thou hast made thy servant king in place of David my father, although I am but a little child [he was about twenty at the time]; I do not know how to go out or come in. . . . Give thy servant therefore an understanding mind to govern thy people, that I may discern between good and evil; for who is able to govern this thy great people?" The Bible tells us that it pleased the Lord that Solomon had asked this, and God said to him, "Because you have asked this, and have not asked for long life or riches or the life of your enemies, but have asked for yourself understanding . . . behold, I now do according to your word. Behold, I give you a wise and discerning mind. . . ." He was also to have riches and honor, for which he did not ask, and God added, "If you will walk in my way, keeping my statutes and my commandments, as your father David walked, then will I lengthen your days" (I Kings 3:5-14).

Solomon was off to a wonderful start! This kingdom, this reign, should have been one of history's highlights. It was a magnificent hour for the kingdom—but it was completely overshadowed and lost because of what was to happen later. If we could only end the story of Solomon here, or better, with the glorious prayer he made at the dedication of the temple, asking God's help in facing apostasy, we would have a story greater than David's!

But we cannot stop here; we must go on to consider the rest of the story. The first downward step that Solomon made could be termed defection. The record reads, "Now King Solomon loved many foreign women: the daughter of Pharaoh, and Moabite, Ammonite, Edomite, Sidonian, and Hittite women, from the nations concerning which the Lord had said to the people of Israel, 'You shall not enter into marriage with them, neither shall they with you, for surely they will turn away your heart after their gods'; Solomon clung to these in love" (I Kings 11:1-2). That was the beginning of his downfall.

The second step was apostasy. That is an ugly word, and many have objected to its use with reference to Solomon. But read the record: "He had seven hundred wives, princesses, and three hundred concubines; and his wives turned away his heart. For when Solomon was old his wives turned away his heart after other gods; and his heart was not wholly true to the Lord his God, as was the heart of David his father. For Solomon went after Ashtoreth the goddess of the Sidonians, and after Milcom the abomination of the Ammonites. . . . Then Solomon built a high place for Chemosh the abomination of Moab, and for Molech the abomination of the Ammonites, on the mountain east of Jerusalem. And so he did for all his foreign wives, who burned incense and sacrificed to their gods" (11:3-8). Because he turned his heart away from God, God had to turn away from Solomon.

The final step was the loss of all that God had given him—or almost all, for God's grace spared some. "And the Lord was angry with Solomon, because his heart had turned away from the Lord, the God of Israel, who had appeared to him twice, and had commanded him concerning this thing, that he should not go after other gods; but he did not keep what the Lord commanded. Therefore the Lord said to Solomon: 'Since this has been your mind and you have not kept my covenant and my statutes which I have commanded you, I will surely tear the kingdom from you and give it to your servant. Yet for the sake of David your father I will not do it in your days, but I will tear it out of the hand of your son. However, I will not tear away all the kingdom; but I will give one tribe to your son for the sake of David my servant, and for the sake of Jerusalem which I have chosen" (11:9-13). That is exactly what happened: the prophet Ahijah came to Jeroboam, took his coat and tore it into twelve pieces and handed Jeroboam ten of them and said, "Take for yourself ten pieces . . ." or ten *tribes*! God had torn the kingdom, and he had given ten parts of it to Solomon's enemy, and only one part was left for Solomon's son.

We learn some powerful lessons here. We learn that God is faithful even though Solomon is faithless. For the sake of David and for the sake of his land, God kept a king on the throne; after Solomon's time, which was about 922 B.C., until 586 B.C., there was a king upon the throne in Jerusalem—a king of the line of David. For the sake of David, God kept His promise.

We learn at the same time that God will not tolerate apostasy and idolatry. As certainly as those elements are brought into the kingdom of Israel, so certainly God must get them out. Solomon could have been a great king—in many respects he was; as far as administration, building, national prestige and international diplomacy are concerned, he went far beyond David. But, in the one thing that was most important, the thing that was the most critical in the life of the nation, in his religious life he suffered a defection and turned away from the Lord. Therefore his kingdom was rent. You can trace a good many of the later sufferings of Israel back to that corruption.

The prophets for three hundred and fifty years after Solomon speak continually about the apostasy of the people. Well, "like king, like people." Solomon imported the wives, the wives imported the gods; Solomon tolerated it, encouraged it, built places of worship for these idolators. What can you expect the people to do but follow along? There is a terrible responsibility in being a national leader. It is a greater responsibility in the eyes of God than in the eyes of men— and the responsibility before man is great enough!

One other practical lesson we may take out of it all: that is, to remember our own national leaders and our own president. We have been charged by the Scriptures to pray for kings and those in authority: we should pray that we may have always at the head of our nation one whose primary interest is not in material splendor, but in doing the will of God, for only then can God bless our nation and use it.

CHAPTER XIII

Elijah

THE PROPHET ELIJAH stands out in the Old Testament as the typical representative of the prophets. When we speak of the Law, we think of Moses; when we speak of the prophets, we think of Elijah. He has been called "Jehovah's answer to Baal" for he came on the scene when Baal worship was at its zenith in Israel. Elijah was one of the two men in Scripture who had the privilege of being taken from this life without passing through death; Enoch was the other. And he was one of the two men granted the honor of standing on the Mount of Transfiguration with Jesus. In this chapter we will think about his times, his work, and his significance to us in the lessons we can learn from him in our own day.

Elijah was a prophet. Just what does that mean? Who were the "prophets"? We have already seen, in our study of Moses that the prophet was God's mouthpiece. If we fail to see the divine origin of the true prophetic message, we fail entirely to understand the phenomenon of prophecy. At the same time, there is a relationship of the prophets to the historical scene that must not be overlooked. The prophets were advisors to the kings. They came on the scene at the moment in history when the kingdom of Israel came into existence, and they continued only as long as that kingdom was in existence. Their primary relationship was to the kingdom.

This important fact is often overlooked, resulting in a hazy notion that prophets belong to the whole Old Testament period. Now I must admit that part of this misunderstanding stems from the fact that the word "prophet," since it basically means "one who has been called [by God to serve as His mouthpiece]," can be used of anyone so called by God, and was so used. Abraham is called a prophet (Genesis 20:7), and so is Moses (Deuteronomy 18:18); yet it would be incorrect to include Abraham and Moses in a list of the Prophets of Israel. Moreover, there were special prophets used by God (cf. Balaam, Numbers 22:35), and there were false prophets who claimed to speak

God's word (Jeremiah 23:16-32). It is equally incorrect to lump these all together and discuss them as "prophets." The prophets, strictly speaking, begin with Samuel (I Samuel 3:20; 9:9), and end with Malachi, so far as the Old Testament is concerned. Then there was a famine of the word of the Lord[1] until John the Baptist appeared in the spirit and power of Elijah to proclaim the coming of the One who would be the fulfillment of all the prophecies concerning the Davidic King. Since He was also the fulfillment of the prophecy in Deuteronomy 18:18 (the Prophet that was to come) as well as the coming King, the offices of prophet and king merge at last into one. But the very fact that Jesus is both Prophet and King serves to underscore our claim that the prophetic office is primarily related to the kingly office.

Another point that is not always clear relates to the writing activities of the prophets. We tend to think of the prophets as the men who wrote the second half of the Old Testament, from Isaiah to Malachi. But there were perhaps just as many prophets who never wrote a line of prophecy—at least, their prophecies have not been preserved for us in Scripture. Samuel, of course, we know; and if we had not thought of it in so many words, we were aware that the Books of Samuel in the Bible are not prophecies.[2] Nathan left no written prophecy; although we are quite familiar with his prophetic utterances to David. We have just read about Ahijah and his prophecy to Jeroboam—but he left no written prophecy. The same can be said for the well-known prophets Elijah and Elisha. And the lesser-known prophets, such as Micaiah ben Imlah (I Kings 22), Gad (I Samuel 22:5), and a number of nameless ones, serve to remind us that God always had His mouth-piece ready to proclaim His word to the king.

Amos is often referred to as the earliest of the writing prophets (c. 760 B.C.). But there had been kings and prophets for two centuries or more by that time. Amos even refers to them (Amos 7:14). As a matter of fact, an important shift in the prophetic office occurred in the eighth century B.C. The prophets before Amos are often called the "oral" or "non-writing" prophets; from Amos on, they are the

[1] This prophetic silence is mentioned in I Maccabees 4:46; 14:41; and had already been of considerable duration, I Maccabees 9:27.

[2] I am aware, of course, that in the Hebrew Bible Joshua, Judges, Samuel, and Kings (I and II) are considered as "The Former Prophets." What I have said about the difference between the "oral" and "writing" prophets can just as truly be said about the difference between the "Former" and the "Latter" Prophets.

"writing" or "literary" prophets. Did you ever ask yourself why there was this important shift from the spoken to the written word?

The prophets, we have seen, were advisors to the kings. The king of Israel was supposed to reign under divine authority, which should have been taken to mean that he was not supposed to act without first determining the will of God on the matter. The prophet was there for that purpose.[3] To make the picture complete, I should also mention the third office: the priest. These three offices, prophet, priest, and king, were supposed to be kept inviolate, each by the other.

The "oral prophets" carried on their prophetic ministry during the period (roughly the tenth and ninth centuries B.C.) when, in spite of the stubbornness of the kings, it seemed that the kingdom might be preserved. The "writing prophets" did not appear until Israel had reached that period of history when there was no longer any hope of preserving the kingdom, even in its split form. With Amos it is obvious that God had determined upon a judgment that would drive the nation into exile. This introduced a new factor: some provision must be made for the preservation of the word of the Lord in permanent form for the day when the nation, or its remnant, would be brought again into the Land. If you study this development carefully, you will notice that Elijah is like the great divide: before him, the prophets sought to advise the kings in order to preserve the kingdom; with Elijah the awful extent of national sin is laid bare. From that time on, the prophets speak of punishment, with only a remnant to be saved.[4]

Elijah appears suddenly, in the seventeenth chapter of First Kings. Without any warning, without any previous introduction, we find Elijah the Tishbite saying to Ahab the king of the Northern Kingdom

---

[3] Other scholars take a broader view of the prophetic office. The *Catholic Commentary on Holy Scripture*, in a splendid article on "Prophetical Literature," suggests on the basis of I Samuel 9:9 and other passages that the prophets were available to the general public for guidance on matters of daily life (§ 411a). Then it goes on to observe that in the *"period of extant prophetical writings . . .* it is almost certainly accidental that there is no mention of prophets being consulted about *private affairs"* (§ 412a). In my estimation, this is an unnecessary confusion arising from an initial failure to define the prophetic office with sufficient precision.

[4] It seems to me utterly unnecessary to try to remove the element of hope and restoration from the eighth century prophets. From the beginning, the writing prophets had but one message: the message of judgment and exile to be visited upon the nation; and from the beginning, the redemptive purpose was apparent in the determination of Jehovah to save the remnant.

that there will be a drought for three years. We know little about Elijah other than the work he did. We are told that he came from Tishbeh: but even the location of Tishbeh is uncertain.

Elijah's ministry was particularly to king Ahab, and it included a number of miracles. That leads us to think a little about miracles. Some of us have had a vague idea that miracles are reported to have occurred intermittently throughout the Old Testament and the New Testament. Actually, this is not so. There are only four distinct periods of miracles that have occurred, and one more yet to come, according to Scripture. In every case, miracles occurred at a time of crisis: when the nation was in bondage in Egypt and about to be exterminated by a cruel and wicked Pharaoh; when the nation was in exile and about to be swallowed up; when the Christ came into the world and was met by the onslaught of Satanic powers; and in the days of the great life-and-death struggle between the forces of Baal and the true worship of Jehovah.

It was at the time of this struggle with Baal that Elijah came on the scene; he went to the king and told him that there would be a drought—no dew or rain for three years, except by his word. And he left him to think about *that*! I suppose Ahab puzzled many times about what took place. Then Elijah went down to the Brook Cherith[5] (I Kings 17:5), and dwelt there for a while, and was ministered to by the ravens who fed him morning and evening—note the miracle! Then the word of the Lord came to Elijah and told him to leave there and go up to Zarephath, which is near Sidon on the Phoenician coast. There he was taken care of by a widow; you recall the story of how he went in and asked her to bring him a little water in a vessel and a little morsel of bread, and how she said, "I have nothing baked, only a handful of meal . . . and a little oil . . . and I am now gathering a couple of sticks, that I may go in and prepare it for myself and my son, that we may eat it, and die" (17:12). Elijah told her that they would not die; that she should feed him first, and the meal and the oil would be continuously and miraculously replenished. And so it was.

The son of the widow became ill and died. The woman did what most of us would do: she turned against Elijah and said, "What have you against me, O man of God? You have come to me to bring

---

[5] Pronounced *kee'rith*. With extremely few exceptions, the *ch* in Scripture names is pronounced as *k*.

my sin to remembrance, and to cause the death of my son!" (17:18).
Elijah turned to God and asked why this had taken place, and then
brought the son back to life again. It was an amazing miracle, the
like of which we might expect to be performed by Jesus, but not by
an Old Testament character. It is also noteworthy that we find very,
very few miracles of such power in the Old Testament.

The time of drought had come and was nearly over, and Elijah was
to go back and face the king and tell him that rain would be sent
to the earth again. The famine was severe in Samaria; and when
Elijah got there he found that the king and one of his servants,
Obadiah,[6] were out looking for a little patch of grass that they could
use to feed the king's mules. The king had gone one way and Obadiah
another, and Elijah met Obadiah and told him to go and proclaim
to Ahab that he had found Elijah. Obadiah said (if we may para-
phrase), "Why do you want me to do that? If I go to Ahab and even
mention your name, you know what's likely to happen to me: the
spirit of the Lord will catch *you* up and take you off somewhere, and
nobody will know where you are, and Ahab will kill me!" But he
went back, nevertheless, under the persuasion of Elijah, and eventually
Ahab came to Elijah and asked, "Is it you, you troubler of Israel?"
(I Kings 18:11-17).

Do you know who Ahab was? He was the son of the man who had
built Samaria: Omri, the greatest king of the Northern Kingdom,
speaking historically. The Scripture does not look upon him that
favorably, because Scripture measures a man by his religious significance, and Omri was not very significant religiously.[7] But the
historical annals of the kings of Assyria for a hundred years after his
day speak about the Northern Kingdom as "the House of Omri." He
was an extremely important man.

When he died, his son Ahab came to the throne and inherited all
of the wealth and splendor and power of that Northern Kingdom
which had been built up by his father. Ahab entered into an alliance
by marrying Jezebel, the daughter of the king of the Phoenicians.
The account is worth careful reading: "And Ahab the son of Omri
did evil in the sight of the Lord more than all that were before him.
And as if it had been a light thing for him to walk in the sins of
Jeroboam the son of Nebat [that was bad enough!], he took to wife

---

[6] Josephus identified him with the prophet Obadiah, but this is unlikely.
[7] Omri rates only a passing reference in the Bible: I Kings 16:21-27.

Jezebel the daughter of Ethbaal king of the Sidonians, and went and served Baal, and worshipped him" (I Kings 16:31).

In those days, when you brought home a wife who served a foreign god, you arranged for the worship of her god. Solomon had done that, and in doing it brought about the downfall of his kingdom; here we have another king doing the same thing. "He erected an altar for Baal in the house of Baal, which he had built in Samaria. And Ahab made an Asherah [a pole, symbolic of the goddess]. Ahab did more to provoke the Lord, the God of Israel, to anger than all of the kings of Israel who were before him." Moreover, he supported, at public expense, four hundred and fifty prophets of Baal and four hundred prophets of Asherah. They ate at the king's table while the people went hungry.

Jezebel was one of the strongest female characters of ancient history —perhaps of all time. She would almost rank with Queen Semiramis of Assyria.[8] Jezebel took it upon herself to try to exterminate the name of Jehovah and His worship from the face of the earth. She considered it her personal mission, it would seem, to get rid of all knowledge of the God of Israel and to replace it with the knowledge and worship of Baal. She almost succeeded. I am not going to suggest that the people of Israel had always hated Baal; many of them had been Baal worshipers before this. We know from the way the prophets had to cry out against Baal worship that there was a good deal of it. But for the first time, under Jezebel, Baal worship became official, and Jehovah worship was something to be stamped out. And just at that moment God set Elijah in the path of Jezebel.

Ahab summoned all the people of Israel and gathered the prophets together at Mt. Carmel for a contest between Baal and Jehovah. Elijah shouted to the people, "How long will you go limping with two different opinions? If the Lord is God, follow him; but if Baal, then follow him." The people did not answer him. And Elijah said, "I, even I only, am left a prophet of the Lord; but Baal's prophets are four hundred and fifty men. Let two bulls be given to us; and let them choose one bull for themselves, and cut it to pieces and lay it on the wood, but put no fire to it; and I will prepare the other bull

---

[8] Of Semiramis Olmstead says, "the most beautiful, most cruel, most power-ful, and most lustful of Oriental queens"—A. T. Olmstead, *History of Assyria* (New York: Charles Scribner's Sons, 1923), p. 158. Semiramis was prominent about twenty-five years after Jezebel's death.

and lay it on the wood, and put no fire to it. And you call on the name of your god and I will call on the name of the Lord; and the God who answers by fire, he is God." The idea of a challenge struck a sympathetic nerve in the people; they said, "It is well spoken!" Then Elijah said to the prophets of Baal, "Choose for yourselves one bull and prepare it, first, for you are many; and call on the name of your god, but put no fire to it." They took the bull and prepared it, and they called on the name of Baal from morning until noon, saying, "O Baal, answer us!" No one answered. And they went limping about the altar which they had made. At noon Elijah taunted them, "Cry aloud, for he is a god; either he is musing, or he has gone aside,[9] or is on a journey, or perhaps he is asleep and must be awakened." So they cried louder, and cut themselves with swords and lances, until the blood gushed out upon them. The sun began to move through the western sky, and they raved on until the time of the offering of the oblation, "but there was no voice; no one answered, no one heeded."

Then Elijah called the people, at about the time of the evening offering, to come to him. He took twelve stones, according to the number of the tribes of the sons of Jacob. Now remember, the nation had already been divided into North and South, into ten tribes and two tribes; but that was not God's ultimate will. To God, Israel was still *one* people. So Elijah built an altar of stones representing one nation. Then he dug a trench about the altar "as great as would contain two measures of seed." He put the wood in place; then he cut the bull in pieces and put it on the wood, and then he said, "Fill four jars with water, and pour it on the burnt offering, and on the wood." And they did. He said, "Do it a second time." And they did it a second time. Elijah said, "Do it a third time." By that time, the water ran around the altar and filled the trench. Then Elijah prayed, "O Lord, God of Abraham, Isaac, and Israel, let it be known this day that thou art God in Israel, and that I am thy servant, and that I have done all these things at thy word." Then the fire of the Lord fell. It consumed the burnt offering and the wood and the stones and the dust, and even licked up the water that was in the trench. When the people saw it they said, "The Lord, he is God . . . ," and they fell

[9] This delicious bit of satire on the earthy nature of Baal is often lost through failure to understand the idiom. Elijah is suggesting that perhaps Baal has "gone to the toilet."

on their faces. Elijah said to them, "Seize the prophets of Baal, let not one of them escape." They were seized and Elijah had them taken down to the brook Kishon and killed.

Now the prophets of Baal were the worshipers of the god who was supposed to be the god of fertility. Baal worship was centered around the idea of fertility; this was the god who gave the corn and the wine and all the rest of life's good things. Hosea ridicules this concept in his prophecy: "She did not know that it was I who gave her the grain, the wine, and the oil, and who lavished upon her silver and gold which they used for Baal" (Hosea 2:8). They thought that by worshiping Baal, they could cause the earth to be fruitful; but for three years there had been no rain and the earth had dried up. The country was enduring a rigorous, terrible famine.

It was therefore not enough that the prophets of Baal be defeated. In addition, Jehovah must show that it is He and not Baal who supplies the country with rain and with food. So Elijah says to Ahab, "Go up, eat and drink; for there is a sound of the rushing of rain." Then Elijah goes up to the top of Mt. Carmel, bows himself to the earth and says to his servant, "Go up now, and look toward the sea." The servant looks and reports, "There is nothing." Elijah says: "Go again seven times." The seventh time the servant says, "Behold, a little cloud like a man's hand is rising out of the sea." Then Elijah, with terrific faith, says, "Go up and say to Ahab, 'Prepare your chariot and go down, lest the rain stop you.'" Now, it had not rained for three years, and there was only a little cloud on the horizon; but Elijah was sure that there was going to be rain before the king could get out of the way! And so there was. They race back to the capital, the rain overtakes them on the way, and they are almost bogged down in the marshy plain of the River Kishon.

There is a postscript to this in the nineteenth chapter. It is interesting because it shows us what kind of men the "heroes of the faith" really were. Here is the man who had been called by God to stand in the way of Jezebel; he had overthrown the prophets of Baal, and brought to naught all of the nonsense of Jezebel. Ahab went back and told Jezebel what Elijah had done, and Jezebel sent a messenger to Elijah and said, "So may the gods do to me, and more also, if I do not make your life as the life of one of them by this time tomorrow." And what did Elijah do? Call down fire from heaven and destroy her, as he had destroyed the messengers of the king? No.

He turned and ran! He was afraid; he fled for his life and went to Beersheba, which is as far south as you can go in that country, and then on beyond that all the way down into the wilderness of Sinai; and he stayed there.

It is amazing, isn't it? How could a man, with all of the power at his command that Elijah had, lose his nerve in the face of this wicked woman? In the still small voice God said to him, "What are you doing here, Elijah?" Elijah replied, "I have been very jealous for the Lord, the God of Hosts; for the people of Israel have forsaken thy covenant, thrown down thy altars, and slain thy prophets with the sword; and I, even I only am left; and they seek my life, to take it away." And God sent him back with a triple mission: to anoint Hazael to be king over Syria, and to anoint Jehu king over Israel, and to anoint Elisha to take his own place as prophet. And God furthermore told him, "I will leave seven thousand in Israel, all the knees that have not bowed to Baal, and every mouth that has not kissed him" (19:18).

One closing scene: Elijah's work on earth was finished. It was time for God to take him up to heaven, and for Elisha to take over as his successor. Elisha did not want to lose his friend and master, and he said, "I will not leave you." For the second time, Elijah tried to leave him, and again Elisha said, "I will not leave you." Finally, when they came down to the river Jordan, Elijah said to Elisha, "Ask what I shall do for you, before I am taken from you." And Elisha said, "I pray you, let me inherit a double share[10] of your spirit." And Elijah said, "You have asked a hard thing; yet if you see me as I am being taken from you, it shall be so for you; but if you do not see me, it shall not be so." As they were talking, behold, a chariot of fire and horses of fire separated the two of them, and Elijah went up by a whirlwind into heaven (II Kings 2:9-12).

One day, nine hundred years later, Elijah stood with Moses on the Mount of Transfiguration and talked with Jesus. What did they talk about? Luke tells us in his ninth chapter. They talked about the departure which Jesus was about to accomplish at Jerusalem (Luke 9:31). Moses had been buried on Mount Nebo let us say fourteen hundred years before that; Elijah had been translated into heaven in

[10] Literally, "two mouths" or two-thirds. This was the portion of the first-born (Deuteronomy 21:17). It is a misinterpretation of this text to try to prove that Elisha was twice as great as Elijah: Scripture never puts Elisha over Elijah!

a whirlwind of fire some nine hundred years before that. Now they were talking with Jesus on the Mount of Transfiguration. Israel was the same old stiff-necked and stubborn people. For fourteen hundred years they had been rejecting the law which God had given them through Moses; for centuries they had been rejecting the word of the prophets of whom Elijah is the representative, and now they were rejecting the word of Jesus. They had stoned the prophets; they had driven them out; they had sawn them asunder; and now they were about to crucify Jesus. But God had not given them up. And Elijah had the chance, as Moses had also, to see that God was still working for the redemption of His people.

CHAPTER XIV

Isaiah

ISAIAH is great for two reasons: he lived in momentous days, in critical days of international upheaval, and he wrote what many consider to be the greatest book in the Old Testament. To understand the reasons for many of the things he said, we must study him in his historic situation.

The first chapter of the prophecy of Isaiah begins with the words, "The vision of Isaiah, the son of Amoz [he is not the prophet *Amos,* but another one whose name is spelled differently in Hebrew], which he saw concerning Judah and Jerusalem in the days of Uzziah, Jotham, Ahaz, and Hezekiah, kings of Judah." To these names we can add Manasseh, for Isaiah probably lived during the first part of the reign of Manasseh. Isaiah's ministry began "in the year that king Uzziah died," and occupied about fifty years.

Those were the days when Tiglath-pileser III came to the throne in Assyria and whipped it into a mighty fighting empire which overran the whole world.[1] He did that first by winning the support of the people of Babylonia; for he did not want the Babylonian king starting a war behind his back. Having made sure of that, he moved toward the west; in a rapid campaign, he took much of Syria and some of the Phoenician cities, and dominated the roads leading to the Phoenician seaports. Israel escaped only by paying a heavy tribute (about $2,000,-000), for which Menahem was allowed to remain as "king." Later, Pekah of Israel and Rezin of Damascus attempted a revolt against Assyria, and Tiglath-pileser moved in promptly, capturing much of Israel, deporting many Israelites, and putting Judah under tribute.[2] We often forget that twelve years before the fall of Samaria, two and a half tribes were carried into captivity. Many of the details are not only

---

[1] For a good resumé, see *Westminster Dictionary of the Bible,* pp. 606-607.

[2] Pul and Tiglath-pileser are the same person. Hence, I Chronicles 5:26 should be translated, "So the God of Israel stirred up the spirit of Pul king of Assyria, *even* the spirit of Tiglath-pileser. . . ," as the verb in the singular indicates: "and *he* carried them away. . . ."

recorded in the Bible, but can be found in Tiglath-pileser's annals as well.[3]

Tiglath-pileser III was followed by Shalmaneser V, the king who beseiged Tyre for five years and the capital of the Northern Kingdom, Samaria, for three years.[4] He was followed, upon his death, by his brother Sargon II, who records in his annals that the first thing he did, in his first year, was to capture Samaria;[5] the Northern Kingdom disappeared. Sargon was followed by Sennacherib, who took forty-six cities of the Southern Kingdom of Judah. He tells us he carried away 200,150 people; he besieged Jerusalem and shut up Hezekiah in the city "as a bird in a cage."[6]

These kings of the Assyrian empire were on the scene at the time Isaiah was carrying on his ministry in a day that was pretty much like our own, when a mighty empire is forming in another part of the world, and threatening the peace of all the world. It went beyond the threatening stage, so far as Israel was concerned.

Turning to the national scene, we have during Isaiah's life the kings Uzziah, Jotham, Ahaz, Hezekiah, and Manasseh. Uzziah had a long and a splendid reign; he was a good king. He made some mistakes, but on the whole his reign was a good one; "he did that which was good in the eyes of the Lord." Jotham was a good king, and Hezekiah was a great king; the Scripture says there was "none like him after him or even before him," probably referring only to the kings of the divided kingdom and not including David and Solomon. Ahaz was the weakest and the most wicked king of the Southern Kingdom and Manasseh had the longest reign in Judah's history and the most apostate.[7]

[3] D. D. Luckenbill, *Ancient Records of Assyria and Babylonia* (Chicago: University of Chicago Press, 1926), Vol. I, §§ 801, 815-16.

[4] For a resumé of Shalmaneser V, see *Unger's Bible Dictionary*, p. 1003.

[5] For a resumé of Sargon II, see *Unger's Bible Dictionary*, pp. 970-972. It now appears (as Olmstead argued over fifty years ago) that Sargon's claim is false, and that Shalmaneser V actually captured Samaria, as the Bible clearly states. This is discussed at length by E. R. Thiele, *The Mysterious Numbers of the Hebrew Kings* (Chicago: University of Chicago Press, 1951), pp. 122-128. For the dates of the kings of Israel and Judah, I am following Thiele.

[6] Luckenbill, *Ancient Records of Assyria and Babylonia*, Vol. II, § 240. For a resumé of Sennacherib, see *Unger's Bible Dictionary* pp. 993-995.

[7] For those who are helped by dates, we give the following:

Uzziah, as regent 791-767, as king 767-740;	Tiglath-pileser III, 745-727
Jotham, as regent 750-740, as king 740-732;	Shalmaneser V, 727-722
Ahaz, as regent 735-732, as king 732-716;	Sargon II, 722-705
Hezekiah, 716-687;	Sennacherib, 705-681
Manasseh, as regent 696-687, as king 687-642.	

No nation is truly strong when it goes to such extremes in the life-time of one man. Such a condition means that things are going to pieces at the heart of the nation. It means that there is nothing to maintain it in balance, that eccentric forces are at work and it is about to fly apart.

Isaiah had his call, according to Isaiah 6:1, in the year that King Uzziah died. That would be about 740 B.C. Isaiah had been a member of the royal court of Uzziah: he had been a scribe of the king (II Chronicles 26:22). As a scribe he knew what was going on. No man in the kingdom had a greater knowledge of what was taking place than the scribe; the king would send to him for the details which it was part of his duty to record. Isaiah was a man in that strategic position. According to tradition, he was not only a scribe; he was also a relative.[8] That is only tradition; but traditions are sometimes true. He was called to his prophetic office in the year that Uzziah died, but he had been on the scene for quite a few years before that.

Let us look at just a few of the highlights of Uzziah's reign. You will find them recorded in II Kings 14 and II Chronicles 26; they are almost parallel accounts, but you should read them side by side to get all of the details.[9] Uzziah is also called Azariah; both names are used in the Scripture. He came to the throne when he was sixteen years of age and he reigned fifty-two years. We are told that he did that which was right in the eyes of the Lord; but we are also told that the high places which had been built under the influence of Baal worship, in the days of Elijah, were not taken down. Now that may seem to be a small matter. But there is an important principle involved, namely, that there is usually a lag between the leader and the followers. When the king or the prophet is good, the people will be slightly less good; when the king and the prophets are evil, the people will be (usually) more evil. Uzziah's failure to remove the high places was an occasion for the religion of the popular level to become further degraded.

In other matters, Uzziah was a great king. He built Elath on the gulf of Aqabah; he waged war against the Philistines; he built the towers of Jerusalem; he had a strong army of 307,500 men and 2600 "mighty" men. But he made one mistake: about twelve years before

---

[8] According to the Talmud, his father Amoz was a brother of King Amaziah, which would make Isaiah and Uzziah cousins. Megillah 10b.

[9] The actual references are: II Kings 14:21—15:7; II Chr. 26:1-23.

the end of his reign, he went into the temple to burn incense—and that was not his privilege. God had very clearly defined the duties of the king, the prophet, and the priest; the king was there to lead the country as a nation, and he had no right to assume the prerogative of the religious office. For this presumption Uzziah was smitten with leprosy. Because he was a leper he could not retain his throne. Jotham became regent in 750; Uzziah continued as nominal king until his death in 740 B.C.

Then followed the reign of Jotham.[10] He had been co-regent for about eleven years, and he reigned beyond that for about three more years. He "did right," according to the Scriptures; he did all that his father had done, except that he did not enter the temple. But again we read that the high places were not taken away and that the people burned incense there. There was still that disease of apostasy gnawing at the heart of the nation.

Then followed the awful days of Ahaz. Many of the prophecies of Isaiah, certainly all those of the first fourteen chapters of the Book of Isaiah, were uttered in the days of this king. To read his record is to read one of the dark pages of Old Testament history.[11] Ahaz came to the throne when he was only twenty years of age, and he reigned sixteen years. We read that he did *not* do that which was right in the eyes of the Lord, but he caused his son to "pass through the fire." To cause your son to pass through the fire meant to offer him as a burnt offering to the god Molech. Ahaz burned his son alive as an offering. He also formed molten images for the Baalim and he burned incense to foreign gods. He went to the war with Pekah, the king of the Northern Kingdom (Israel), and with Rezin, the king of Damascus. To Rezin he lost Elath, which had been built by his grandfather Uzziah. He suffered a crushing defeat.

There was also an Edomite and a Philistine invasion in the days of Ahaz, and in the face of all of this pressure from the Northern Kingdom, Damascus, the Edomites, and the Philistines, Ahaz decided that the best thing he could do was to call for help from the one nation that was strong, namely Assyria. He cried out for Tiglath-pileser to come over and help him. Well, we know what can happen when some little nations get quarrelling over territory, and one of the little nations asks a strong nation to come to its aid. We have seen

[10] For Jotham, read II Kings 15:7-38; II Chronicles 20:23—27:9.
[11] For Ahaz, read II Kings 15:38—16:20; II Chronicles 27:9—28:27.

it in our own time. Tiglath-pileser seized the opportunity; he moved immediately, and took Damascus. Ahaz made a journey from Jerusalem to Damascus to meet with Tiglath-pileser, and Tiglath-pileser said, "Sure, we'll support you—if you pay for it." To pay out money, it was necessary for Ahaz practically to strip the temple of all of its wealth—which he did.

That was not all. While Ahaz was in Damascus, a beautiful altar caught his eye, and he had the plans copied and sent back to Jerusalem. He had that magnificent bronze altar which Solomon had built taken out of the temple, and replaced with a copy of the heathen altar from Damascus.

Then he closed the doors of the house of the Lord. No more sacrifices. No more offerings. No more incense burned. The people could not even worship God!

During these days, Isaiah was prophesying. He had gone to Ahaz and told him to ask a sign from the Lord against Rezin and Pekah (Isaiah 7); Ahaz refused, and Isaiah replied that God would give him a sign anyway. "Behold, a young woman[12] shall conceive and bear a son . . . (and) before the child knows how to refuse the evil and choose the good . . ." these two smoking firebrands will be extinguished. And Isaiah went to the prophetess (I understand that to refer to his wife), and she conceived and she bore a son and they called the name of the child Maher-shalal-hash-baz; and before that child had even grown to the age of knowing the difference between right and wrong, this thing was over. But Ahaz did not believe that sign; he was not a man of faith. He believed that he could work out the situation by international diplomacy.

After that came the days of Hezekiah, and it is a joy to read the record of Hezekiah after you have read the awful story of Ahaz.[13] Hezekiah did that which was right. He removed the high places. Even the brazen serpent of Moses, which had been erected in the wilderness, and which had been set up again and was being worshiped as an idol, Hezekiah broke in pieces. We read that "after him there was none like him." He opened the doors of the house of the

---

[12] I have elsewhere published my reasons in detail for the translation "young woman" rather than "virgin" in Isaiah 7:14. The sign was to be immediately valid to Ahaz—which certainly was not to be a virgin birth in his day! The virgin birth of Jesus was a greater fulfillment of this sign (for "young woman" can also apply in the case of a virgin birth).

[13] For Hezekiah, read II Kgs. 16:20; 18:1—20:21; II Chr. 28:27—32:33.

Lord (II Chronicles 29:3-19), and he had the priests go in and clean out the rubbish that was there. It took them eight days to cleanse the temple and when it was spotless again, Hezekiah offered a magnificent sacrifice; he gathered the people of Israel and Judah together to celebrate Passover, a feast neglected for a long, long time. It was too late to have it at the regular, or "official" time, and he prayed the Lord that they might be allowed to have a Passover the following month. And he even went so far as to invite the people of the Northern Kingdom with whom the King before him had been at war to come to Jerusalem for their Passover. And many of them came, and there was rejoicing and there was weeping.

I remember one day in 1952, standing on top of Mt. Gerizim, where the Samaritans were holding their Passover. Some of the Samaritans live on the Israeli side of the country today; most of them, of course, live on the Arab side. There had been no crossing over that border for five years; from 1948 on, there had been no Passover celebration for the Samaritans in Israel. But in 1952 they opened the border for the first time. I was talking to the Samaritan high priest and the other priests with him when the first carload of Samaritans came through; they were squealing and laughing and singing and going through all sorts of antics to express their joy. Here they were, having a Passover celebration for the first time in five years! I think something like that must have taken place on a much vaster scale in the days of Hezekiah.

And yet it was only a year or two after this that Shalmaneser came up and besieged the Northern Kingdom. For three years he laid siege to Samaria, and then it fell. The Northern Kingdom was gone, the ten tribes completely dispersed over the face of the earth. Isaiah had a message for that. He also had a message for Hezekiah. But Hezekiah would not listen. He staged a rebellion against the Assyrians, and Sennacherib came and gave him a good drubbing, and once more Israel paid tribute to the Assyrians. They stripped what was left of the temple furnishings to pay the bill.

Then Hezekiah fell sick; and Isaiah came to tell him that it was to be the end of his life (II Kings 20:1). But Hezekiah repented and said, "Remember now, O Lord, I beseech thee, how I have walked before thee in faithfulness and with a whole heart, and have done what is good in thy sight" (verse 3). Then God gave Isaiah the marvelous message of a sign from God that he would live another fifteen years. If the shadow on the sundial of Ahaz moved backward instead of forward, this would happen. The sign came; God repented; the shadow moved backwards, and Hezekiah was spared.

Then Hezekiah lost his head. He welcomed certain "emissaries" from Merodach-baladan, king of Babylon, who had come to congratulate him on his recovery. If Hezekiah had been thinking he would have recognized them for spies. He was not thinking; he gave them a royal welcome, showed them everything he had—and of course they reported to Merodach-baladan that there was yet great wealth in Jerusalem, free for the taking.

Isaiah was furious; he told Hezekiah of the blow that would fall on his people for all this: not only would their wealth fall to Babylon but the people themselves would go captive (Isaiah 39:1-8). And so it was.

Isaiah saved Hezekiah, in another bad situation. Rabshakah, who was Sennacherib's commander-in-chief, taunted the men of Hezekiah as he stood in siege at their walls. He told them to stop asking God to save them, for God had sent the Assyrians to punish them! In panic, Hezekiah's captains begged the Assyrian to speak in Aramaic instead of Hebrew, so the people would not know what was going on. It certainly looked like the end for Hezekiah. He rushed to Isaiah and asked, "What shall I do?" Isaiah replied in effect, "Don't worry; the Lord will not allow him to take Jerusalem." Sennacherib himself came and encamped outside Jerusalem, and according to his own proud boast he had Hezekiah shut up in that city "like a bird in a cage"—but the angel of the Lord visited Sennacherib's camp at night. Herodotus, the Greek historian, tells us that mice came and ate all the strings on their bows, and their shields, and they were unable to wage their war, and they had to leave.[14] And Hezekiah was spared.

We shall not say much about Manasseh. We do not know how far into Manasseh's reign Isaiah lived, but we do know that not long after Manasseh came to the throne he began to do the evil recorded of his reign: he rebuilt the high places, and the altars of Baal. He did what no one before him had done: he brought in all sorts of occultism and spiritism; he worshiped idols and demons, and he shed a great deal of blood (II Kings 21). According to Jewish tradition he had

[14] Some have interpreted the Scripture to mean, in the light of this reference to mice (equals rats?), that Bubonic plague was the cause of Sennacherib's defeat.

Isaiah killed, sawed in half. It may be that Isaiah is the one who is referred to in Hebrews 11:32 where we are told that "They . . . were sawn in two."

What was the message of this man in these tremendous days? Here was the nation coming to its end, with things going to pieces all around it; the Northern Kingdom was gone, the armies of the Assyrians were encamped around Jerusalem, and forty-six cities of the country southwest of Jerusalem had been conquered by that same Assyrian king. What was Isaiah's message in the face of all this?

First of all, it was a message of the sovereignty of God. God sits on His throne and rules this world. "In the year that King Uzziah died, I saw the Lord." Uzziah was dead, but God was not. He was on His throne, high up and lifted up.

It was a message of the sinfulness of the people. The first five chapters of Isaiah's prophecy talk about that, and it is all nicely summarized at the end of the sixth chapter, when God comes to Isaiah and gives him his vision and says, "Go and tell this people." Isaiah asks, "What shall I say?" and God says (we translate freely): "Tell them that though they hear, they will not understand; that they see but they will not perceive; that their heart is fat, their ears are heavy, their eyes are shut, and they just refuse to understand." A hopeless kind of ministry, isn't it?

The third element of his message is that this sovereign God, who sits in the heavens and who reigns in spite of all that is happening here on earth, uses the Gentiles to punish Israel. He talks about that in the tenth chapter of Isaiah, and in several other chapters. God is the one who has brought the rod of the Assyrian against these people. He is the one who is using even the unbelieving pagans to smite His sinful people because of their sins.

You say it is a terrible message; is that *all* he has to say? No; in Isaiah 40 we find a message of the mercy of God. "Comfort, comfort my people, says your God. Speak tenderly to Jerusalem, and cry to her that her warfare is ended, that her iniquity is pardoned, that she has received from the Lord's hand double for all her sins." And he goes on to talk in chapters 42, 49, 50 to 53 about the "suffering servant." There is a lot of discussion about who that suffering servant is. Is it Israel? Certainly Israel was the Lord's servant; certainly Israel was suffering. But there are other passages that would seem to indicate that it is not only Israel, but one of the Israelites, one representative

Israelite, who in a supreme way is the Lord's Servant. He is the one who takes upon Himself the guilt and the burden of this people.

Isaiah's message is a message of salvation. Notice how he pulls the whole thing together. This sovereign God who uses a Gentile king to destroy His people, uses another Gentile king (Cyrus, the Persian) to bring them back again (Isaiah 45:1). He talks about the days when there will be a Son (Isaiah 9:6-7) who will be the mighty God, the everlasting Father, the Prince of Peace. There will be Immanuel, not the son of the prophetess, but the greater Immanuel, who will come to spare His people; and the suffering Servant becomes the Sin-bearer of Israel. He talks in the last few chapters (58 through 66) of the glory that will be theirs. It is a magnificent message. It is a message that starts with the sinfulness of the people and tells them that God is going to punish them double for all their iniquities; but it goes on to talk of the redemption and the glory which will come to the remnant who are faithful to the Lord.

I have already suggested that in many ways our day is like Isaiah's day. We are seeing nations collapse all about us. If we were living in England or France instead of in America, we would see it even more clearly. I do not know whether God is going to use the scourge of Russia to punish America for her godlessness and sinfulness; I am not a prophet. It may well be. He has done it before. I believe that He used the scourge of Nazi Germany to punish the unbelieving nations of Europe, and it may well be that you and I will see our nation—I pray God that we shall not!—punished by God for our sin. No nation can stand against Him and defy Him.

But if by chance that punishment should come, we have a message that looks beyond it, that tells us that the end of this world is not punishment and destruction; the end is glory and the Kingdom of God. Isaiah could look down across those years and see the nations about him falling one after another, and he could say, "This ultimately is going to come *here,* and God will carry away your sons and your daughters and the wealth of your temple." But he could also look past that and say, "The time will come when the nations will turn their swords into plowshares and their spears into pruning hooks, and when the nations will come up to Jerusalem to worship." Just so, we can look beyond the present time of crisis and say, "This is God's will, because after all, it is God who sits on the throne, and this is His world."

CHAPTER XV

Jeremiah

JEREMIAH is certainly one of the greatest of the prophets. Some consider him to be the most Christlike man to appear before the Lord Jesus Himself. I would not be honest if I failed to add that others look upon him as mentally deranged. Certainly he lived in one of the most turbulent periods of history this world has ever seen, with three large nations and countless smaller groups waging wars, conducting raids, and stirring up all sorts of intrigues. He lived under seven kings of Judah, and performed his ministry under five of them. He witnessed one of the greatest religious revivals in the history of Israel; he also witnessed three invasions of Jerusalem and the utter destruction of the city. Meanwhile, two of the great nations, Egypt and Assyria, had fallen to the third, Babylonia. And certainly Jeremiah had one of the most discouraging tasks ever handed out to man. He was commanded to persuade his people to allow themselves to be taken into captivity.

Jeremiah is often described as the "weeping prophet." As a matter of fact, his name has given us a word in the English language, "jeremiad" which means "a tale of woe," or sorrow or disappointment. We know more about Jeremiah personally than we do of any other prophet because there are so many personal references in his prophecy.

He was called to the office when he was a young man, approximately twenty years of age. But God told him, "Before I formed you in the womb I knew you, and before you were born I consecrated you, I appointed you a prophet to the nations" (1:5). Jeremiah did not have the experiences which most young men have; these were denied him because of his calling. He says, "I did not sit in the company of merrymakers, nor did I rejoice; I sat alone, because thy hand was upon me, for thou hast filled me with indignation" (15:17).

Judging from his extremely emotional and sentimental character, we would conclude that he was the kind of man who would have profited very much from having a wife and family. Yet he was forbidden to marry: "The word of the Lord came to me: 'You shall not take a wife, nor shall you have sons or daughters in this place. For thus says the Lord concerning the sons and daughters who are born in this place, and concerning the mothers who bore them and the fathers who begot them in this land: They shall die with deadly diseases. They shall not be lamented, nor shall they be buried; they shall be as dung on the surface of the ground. They shall perish by the sword and by famine, and their dead bodies shall be food for the birds of the air and for the beasts of the earth' " (16:1-4). It was such a terrible, calamitous time that God in effect said to Jeremiah, "You must not enter into these experiences. You shall not have a wife and family."

Jeremiah lived in the days of the greatest revival that Israel ever knew—we shall discuss that when we consider Josiah the king. And yet, Jeremiah had a message not of joy, not of exultation because of this great revival; he had a message of gloom and doom, a message from which he himself shrank. He did not want to proclaim such words. Listen to his cry: "O Lord, thou hast deceived me, and I was deceived; thou art stronger than I, and thou hast prevailed. I have become a laughingstock all the day; everyone mocks me. For whenever I speak, I cry out, I shout, 'Violence and destruction!' For the word of the Lord has become for me a reproach and derision all day long. If I say, 'I will not mention him, or speak any more in his name,' there is in my heart as it were a burning fire shut up in my bones, and I am weary with holding it in, and I cannot. For I hear many whispering. Terror is on every side! 'Denounce him! Let us denounce him!' say all my familiar friends, watching for my fall. . . . But the Lord is with me as a dread warrior" (20:7-11). He asked God why he should force him to give a message such as this. The whole twentieth chapter is a chapter of lament. "Cursed be the day on which I was born! The day when my mother bore me, let it not be blessed! Cursed be the man who brought the news to my father! . . ."

He just did not want to be responsible for a message such as this; and yet God had laid it upon him, and it is to his credit that he proclaimed the message faithfully. In fact, when reading Jeremiah we have to distinguish between the complaints of Jeremiah and the message of God: "If you return, I will restore you, and you shall stand before me. If you utter what is precious, and not what is worthless, you shall be as my mouth. They shall turn to you, but you shall not turn to them. And I will make you to this people a fortified wall of bronze; they will fight against you, but they shall not prevail over you, for I am with you to save you and deliver you, says the Lord (15:19-20). When we are reading this prophecy, we must keep in mind that some of the words in the book are the prophet's own objections to the message he has to give: they are the outpourings of his own feelings; the rest of the time— most of the time—it is the message which God has laid upon him.

It was only after he had preached for many years that his message was put into writing. Chapter 36 tells us about that. In the fourth year of Jehoiakim, which was many years after he had started to preach, the word came to Jeremiah from the Lord, "Take a scroll and write on it all of the words that I have spoken to you against Israel and Judah and all the nations. . . ." Jeremiah dictated it to Baruch the scribe, and it was then read to the king. As the king heard it, column by column, he ordered it to be cut up and thrown in the fire, until the whole thing was burned. He wanted nothing to do with a message like that. But at the word of the Lord the entire thing was written all over again, with certain additions, before it came into the form that we have now in the Scriptures.

Jeremiah saw the captivity which took place when Nebuchadrezzar,[1] the king of Babylon, invaded Jerusalem and carried off the nobles of the people and the vessels from the temple. But because he had preached to the people to yield to Babylon (he recognized that it was God's will that they should go into captivity) Jeremiah was granted certain privileges: "Nebuchadrezzar . . . gave command concerning Jeremiah through Nebuzaradan, the captain of the guard, saying 'Take him, look after him well and do him no harm, but deal with him as he tells you'" (39:11). He gave Jeremiah his choice: he could go to Babylon or he could stay in Jerusalem. He chose to stay in Jerusalem, and he had the protection of the king of Babylon there not because he was selling out to the Babylonians, but because he had proclaimed the message of God that there was no use trying to fight against this. It was God's will that the people should be taken into Babylon and into captivity.

He preached a message of "life as usual." In the days when the Babylonian flag was flown over Jerusalem, there was a false prophet named Hananiah who said, "Thus saith the Lord of hosts, the God of

---

[1] Both "Nebuchadnezzar" and "Nebuchadrezzar" are found in the Bible, the latter in Jeremiah. The difference is apparently due to a dialectal dissimilation which need not concern us here. Jeremiah's form more nearly reflects the Babylonian *Nabû-kudurri-uṣur*.

Israel: I have broken the yoke of the king of Babylon. Within two years I will bring back to this place all the vessels of the Lord's house, which Nebuchadnezzar, king of Babylon took away from this place . . . I will also bring back Jeconiah. . . , and all the exiles . . ." (28:2-4). Jeremiah would have gladly said "Amen" to that, but he said, "Let us wait and see." At the end of two years, it had not happened. It was a false message that God had not given to Hananiah, and Hananiah died for uttering such rebellion. Jeremiah gave the true message in the next chapter: "Thus says the Lord of hosts, the God of Israel, to all the exiles whom I have sent into exile from Jerusalem to Babylon: Build houses and live in them; plant gardens and eat their produce. Take wives and have sons and daughters; take wives for your sons, and give your daughters in marriage. . . ; multiply there, and do not decrease." And he goes on to say, "When seventy years are completed for Babylon, I will visit you, and I will fulfill to you my promise and bring you back to this place" (29:4-10).

Jeremiah was so convinced that this was true—that God was going to bring His people back at the end of seventy years—that he himself caused a plot of ground to be purchased at Anathoth, which would be used for those who would return from the captivity. He reminds us somewhat of Abraham, in that respect: Abraham knew that his descendants would be slaves in a foreign land for four hundred years, and yet he bought a plot of ground as a burial place for his wife and himself against the day when his family would come back to that land, and when it would be theirs.

In the days of Jeremiah, the closing days of the kingdom, there was a pro-Egypt party. They felt that their hope was Egypt, that they could stand off the forces of Babylonia if they would unite with Pharaoh. Jeremiah had not gone along with that idea, because he knew that God's will was otherwise and that God had explicitly said that they should not trust in Egypt. The pro-Egypt party felt that he was a traitor, that he was selling out. They left the land, finally, after an unsuccessful attempt to overthrow the Babylonian puppet on the throne, and they took Jeremiah to Egypt with them. He tells us about it in the forty-third chapter. He was then about sixty years of age, and he had been prophesying for perhaps forty years. He was in Egypt for a few years, but we know practically nothing about him during that time. He prophesied a bit more; and then he died there, a man hated by his fellow countrymen, a man whose life was lived under terrific pressure of saying things he did not want to say, a man ridiculed by the people and repudiated by the king; even Josiah—the great king, the king who was responsible for the great revival—seems to have turned against him at one time. Jeremiah was a lonely man, but a man of God.

Let us look closely at the day in which he lived. He came to the prophetic office when Josiah was king. Josiah had acceded to the throne at the age of eight, and had been converted in the eighth year of his reign and had become "out and out for the Lord." It was in the thirteenth year of the reign of Josiah that Jeremiah was called to the prophetic office at twenty years of age; Josiah was about the same age and his great efforts to clean up the country were getting into full swing. If I were to be called by God to be a prophet, I could want nothing better than to come to my job at a time when the leadership of the nation was undergoing a real spiritual revival and the nation was beginning to cleanse itself; I would consider that to be a most auspicious moment to begin a prophetic task. It would seem as though I could not fail; I could join hands with a king of my own age and we could go ahead and sweep the nation into a glorious revival. That was the potential of the moment. In the eighteenth year of Josiah—that would be five years after Jeremiah had come on the scene—his workmen, in cleaning out the temple, discovered the Law: the Law of Moses which had been lost in the rubbish! You can imagine how low the spiritual character of the nation had fallen when the rubbish that cluttered up the temple had buried even the copy of the Law. When they read it to Josiah, he broke into tears; he realized that God must certainly punish the nation for having failed to obey the Law which He had given (cf. II Kings 22:1-13).

Recognizing the great sin, Josiah sent to Huldah the prophetess to ask her what was going to happen now; she assured him that God certainly would punish these people, but that it would not happen in his day because of his true penitence and his desire to walk in the way of the Lord. In gratitude, Josiah put down the idolatrous priests, destroyed the altar which Jeroboam had built at Bethel, banished the mediums and the wizards and the idols and abominations, and held a Passover such as had not been held since the days of Samuel: apparently, it even exceeded the glory of the one that Hezekiah had held in Isaiah's day (cf. II Kings 23:1-25).

But Josiah, somewhere along the line, got out of contact with Jeremiah and with the will of God, and he very foolishly tried to interfere with an invasion of Pharaoh-Neco, the king of Egypt;[2] he was killed at Megiddo by Neco's archers. He was succeeded by Jehoahaz; all we can say about him is that he did evil, and that Neco deposed him and carried him off to Hamath, and thence to Egypt. Jehoahaz was succeeded by Jehoiakim, a puppet whom Neco had placed on the throne, who also did evil; he laid the whole land under tribute to Egypt. It was in his days that Nebuchadrezzar first invaded the country and made Jehoiakim his vassal, replacing him three years later, when he attempted to revolt, with Jehoiachin, another puppet. He also did evil. He was carried away by Nebuchadrezzar, who then put Zedekiah, yet another puppet, on the throne (II Kings 24:1-20).

We read in the closing verses of Jeremiah that when Evil-merodach succeeded to the throne of Babylon after the days of Nebuchadrezzar, he took Jehoiachin out of prison and he fed him daily rations (Jeremiah 52:31-34). For a long, long time, that statement was suspect; no king of Babylon would do a thing like that! But not too many years ago a cuneiform tablet was discovered in the gate of the city of Babylon, which contained the orders of King Evil-merodach, to grant daily portions to Yaukin, the King of Judah (that is Jehoiachin), and to his sons.[3] So we have archaeological confirmation that this element of the story is historical. Zedekiah lived through the days when all of the wealth and the best men of the city were carried to Babylon: the princes, the mighty men, the craftsmen. No one was left but the poorest. Finally, when Zedekiah tried to revolt, Nebuchadrezzar sent his troops to sack the city, burning the temple, the palace, and every great house, and tearing down the walls. Zedekiah was blinded and carried in chains to Babylon. Jeremiah's prophecies were largely in the days of Josiah and Zedekiah. As you read through the book you will notice that these are the names most often mentioned.

---

[2] There has been some confusion concerning Neco's purpose and why Josiah got himself involved. The best suggestion is that Neco was going not "against" but "to the aid of" Assyria (II Kings 23:29). Nineveh had already fallen to the Medes and Babylonians and Neco was either attempting to aid the remaining Assyrian forces, or (more likely) trying to take some territory for Egypt. Just why Josiah attempted to interfere is not clear; a simple explanation would be that he was trying to protect his own land against an Egyptian land-grab.

[3] Described by W. F. Albright, "King Joiachin in Exile," *Biblical Archaeologist*, Vol. 5 (1942), pp. 51-55. The tablets had been discovered and taken to Berlin in the early part of this century, but had not been read until E. F. Weidner made this remarkable discovery in 1933. The translation is in Pritchard, *Ancient Near Eastern Texts*, p. 308.

This gives you a pretty good idea of Jeremiah's day. It was a day when the forces of Egypt and the forces of Assyria were slugging it out for supremacy; actually, the forces of Babylonia were the winners, because all that Egypt and Assyria did was weaken each other, and Babylonia was able to come in and pick up the pieces. It was a day when the nation of Judah was having its last chance before God, and when God had decided that Judah must pay the penalty for its idolatry, its apostasy, its bloodshed, and its evil. Jeremiah came on the scene with a message—a message which so completely oppressed him that there are some who think that Jeremiah was a psychopathic case. I was present in New York a few years ago at the meeting of a learned society, when one of the papers read at the meeting attempted to psychoanalyze Jeremiah. I do not know enough about psychiatry to give the details but I am certain that if Jeremiah had not been the Lord's servant, he might well have been a neurotic. Anyone who had to face situations such as he faced and deliver the messages he delivered certainly would be torn by the pressures of all sorts of emotions! You have no doubt heard the claim from time to time that there are more people in mental hospitals because of religion than any other single reason. I do not know whether there are figures to substantiate such a claim. But this much, I think, is clear: such cases do not develop in persons who are certain that they *are* doing God's will; rather it is the persons who are torn with fears that they have *not* done God's will who break down. Professor Hyatt has well observed, with reference to Jeremiah: "On account of his deep faith in God, and because he did not hesitate to give vent to his feelings of despair and bitterness, the tension of his inner life did not cause him to break down."[4]

Turning to Jeremiah's message, we can say that it was a message of denunciation. In chapter 7, he declares that God wants obedience. The Judeans were practicing a formal kind of religion. He says, "Thus says the Lord of hosts, the God of Israel: 'Add your burnt offerings to your sacrifices, and eat the flesh. For in the day that I brought them out of the land of Egypt, I did not speak to your fathers or command them concerning burnt offerings and sacrifices. But this command I gave them, "Obey my voice, and I will be your God, and you shall be my people; and walk in all the way that I command you that it may be well with you." ' " He goes on to point out that they did not walk in His way; they did not obey. They backslid; they went their own

[4] *Interpreter's Bible,* Vol. 5, p. 783.

way. "From the day that your fathers came out of the land of Egypt to this day, I have persistently sent all my servants the prophets to them, day after day; yet they did not listen to me, or incline their ear, but stiffened their neck. They did worse than their fathers" (Jeremiah 7:21-25). God did not want formality; He wanted obedience.

Some would have us believe that Jeremiah represented an anti-priest movement in Judah. The "Book of the Law," discovered in Josiah's temple-cleaning, they tell us, was a newly-written document (known to us as Deuteronomy), that was an attempt to get "Scriptural" backing for the rising priesthood. It is clear, they point out, that Jeremiah was opposed to burnt offerings and sacrifices. But this would have been impossible, they remind us, if the Law of Moses had already been written including these things, for then Jeremiah would have been branded as a false prophet. Of course we might ask, If the priestly caste became powerful enough to impose its will on the Jewish people, how did the prophetic message manage to survive? Most of the prophets, it seems to me, oppose what Jeremiah is opposing. Or we might ask, How did the priestly caste ever get started? The prophets from Amos on opposed meaningless ritual. The best answer is the easiest answer, for it is clear that the prophets were voicing God's protest against form without content, ritual without true religion, offerings without obedience. The priestly ritual was not something new; it was something old, so old that it had become cold, meaningless formality. God hates such ritual (Amos 5:21). He wants worship that stems from the heart (Micah 6:6-8). Jeremiah was uttering this same message, which God's servants the prophets had been proclaiming for more than a century.

Jeremiah reminded them that God had never intended it to be a matter of religious furniture: "And when you have multiplied and increased in the land, in those days, says the Lord, they shall no more say, 'The ark of the covenant of the Lord'" (Jeremiah 3:16). It is a matter of something deeper than that; it reaches to the depths of the heart: "O Jerusalem, wash your heart from wickedness, that you may be saved. How long shall your evil thoughts lodge within you?" (4:14). It is the heart that is wicked. It is the heart that needs to be changed. We are told sometimes that this is a New Testament message; perhaps it is. Jeremiah in some respects comes closest to the New Testament message with his attitude toward religion. He talked about the day when there would be a new covenant: "Behold, the days are coming, says the Lord, when I will make a new covenant with the house of

Israel and the house of Judah, not like the covenant which I made with their fathers when I took them by the hand to bring them out of the land of Egypt. . . . But this is the covenant which I will make with the house of Israel after those days, says the Lord: I will put my law within them, and I will write it in their hearts; and I will be their God, and they shall be my people. And no longer shall each man teach his neighbor and each his brother, saying, 'Know the Lord,' for they shall all know me, from the least of them to the greatest . . ." (31:31-33). And again: "I will give them one heart and one way, that they may fear me forever, for their own good and the good of their children after them" (32:39). That summarizes the message of Jeremiah. It is a message of punishment and gloom and doom, but it is also a message of hope and restoration and a day when God will take away all of the formal aspects of religion and put a genuine heart-religion in His people.

One day Jesus said to His disciples, "Who do men say that the Son of Man is?" And they said, "Some say . . . Jeremiah." Well, there were qualities of Jesus that were like the qualities of Jeremiah. He too wept over Jerusalem. He too was crushed in His heart by the sins of the people. But I think there is one outstanding difference between them —and it is a difference that we should not overlook when we try to evaluate Jeremiah the prophet. Jeremiah had only words of vengeance for his enemies. For example, "O Lord of hosts, who judgest righteously, who triest the heart and the mind, let me see thy vengeance upon them, for to thee have I committed my cause" (11:20); or again: "O Lord, thou knowest; remember me and visit me, and take vengeance for me on my persecutors . . ." (15:15). But Jesus, when He was persecuted, turned and prayed to the Father, "Father, forgive them, for they know not what they are doing." In Jeremiah we see a great man; we do not see completely the love of the Son of God. He approaches it; in many respects he approaches it more than any other in the Old Testament. But he comes just so far, and then falls short.

CHAPTER XVI

Ezekiel

To MANY, Ezekiel is a little-known person, and his book an unknown book. If we look for the reason, we have only to read the first chapter of Ezekiel with its four-faced creatures and its wheels within wheels. If that is not convincing, to read the gloomy prophecies of judgment and destruction that occupy the first half of the book will certainly deter many from finishing the book. However, as in the case of Daniel and Revelation (with which Ezekiel has much in common), we must learn to fasten upon the understandable rather than to be confused by the enigmatic; we must learn to look at the glorious outcome, rather than to be repelled by (or possibly gloat over) the scenes of judgment. When we learn to read these books in such a way, then we shall find that they are truly great books. Of such, Charles R. Erdman, dean of American Bible expositors, writes as the opening words of his book on Ezekiel, "Blessed are those poets and prophets who have taught the people of God to sing songs in the night."[1]

Ezekiel was the prophet whose lot it was to live with his people in captivity. It was his burden to have to foretell in detail the destruction of Jerusalem. It was his sad experience to see, in a vision, the glory of the Lord departing from the temple, and it was his happy experience to see that same glory returning to the new temple. One day, many years later, when the church of the Lord Jesus Christ was facing the black night of persecution by the Roman emperors, when the aged John was sitting in exile on the isle of Patmos, he had a vision of the horrors of judgment and the glories of the triumph and he wrote the book of Revelation. There can be little doubt that he found the source of much of his hope in the prophecy of Ezekiel.

What do we know about the prophet Ezekiel? He was the son of Buzi, he was a priest, and he was with the exiles in Tel-Abib[2] in

[1] C. R. Erdman, *The Book of Ezekiel* (Westwood, N. J.: Fleming H. Revell Co., 1956), p. 9.

[2] The dictionary authorizes the pronunciation *tell-ă'-bĭb* for this name; however, since it has been taken for the name of the modern Israeli city of Tel Aviv, I see no reason why we should not give it the modern pronunciation of *tell-ă-veev'*.

154

Babylonia (1:1-3; 3:15). Ezekiel had been exiled with the group that had been taken captive with Jehoiachin: a group that is described as princes, mighty men of valor, craftsmen and smiths, officials and chief men of the land (II Kings 24:14). He therefore had a place of some prominence in his nation. If the opening reference to "the thirtieth year" refers to his age at the time of his call—which seems the best of all explanations given—we can say that Ezekiel was born about 621 B.C., and that he was twenty-five years old when he was taken into captivity. For a man of thirty, Ezekiel was unusually mature, probably due to the fact that he had lived through thirty hectic years. By the time Ezekiel was fourteen, his nation was paying tribute to Egypt. During the next ten years he saw four kings on the throne, and the controls passed from Egypt to Babylonia; he saw two kings deposed, and at least one severely punished for trying to lead a revolt. He saw the golden furnishings and then the golden decoration of the temple stripped away to pay tribute to the foreign governments. Finally, he himself was taken to Babylonia in captivity.

What was life in exile like? Those who were exiled by the Assyrians (the Northern Kingdom, for example) were scattered abroad, and, so far as we can ascertain, soon lost their identities. On the other hand, the Babylonians seem to have allowed their displaced persons to settle in communities and to pursue a rather normal existence. They built houses, planted vineyards, pursued their crafts, and so forth. Jeremiah had been instructed to advise the Jews to do just these things (Jeremiah 29:4-7). Some of the Jews in exile quickly grew to like their new surroundings. They were probably impressed with the fertile plains well watered by the system of canals then in existence,[3] in contrast to the stony hills of Palestine from which man could scarcely wrest his existence. They must have liked the cultural factors, especially the opportunities for business enterprise, for within a generation we find records of business houses having Jewish names.[4] Since they accumulated considerable wealth, as evidenced by the handsome contributions made for rebuilding the temple (cf. Ezra 2:68-69), we can suppose that the burden of taxation was not excessive. These factors must have

[3] The river Chebar (1:3) might be translated "The Grand Canal."

[4] H. Gressmann, *Altorientalische Texte zum Alten Testamente* (Berlin and Leipzig, 1926), pp. 434f. For a good picture of the living conditions among the exiles, read P. Heinisch, *History of the Old Testament* (Collegeville, Minn.: The Liturgical Press, 1952), pp. 310-314.

entered into the decision of many Jews not to return to Palestine when they had the opportunity under Cyrus the Great. History since the days when Abraham went out from Ur, seems to have come around the cycle. Will God be able to get His people out of Mesopotamia a second time?

One of the distinctly depressing features of the exile, at least to the more religious of the deportees, was the feeling that they were absent from the Lord. It is hard for us to realize that the people of God had not yet learned the great truth of the universality or omnipresence of God. As it was in the case of Ruth and her daughters-in-law, so it was with the exiles in Ezekiel's day: to leave the land of promise was to leave the Lord who had given them that land.

> By the waters of Babylon,
>   there we sat down and wept,
>   when we remembered Zion.
> On the willows there
>   we hung up our lyres.
> For there our captors
>   required of us songs,
> and our tormentors, mirth, saying,
>   "Sing us one of the songs of Zion!"
> How shall we sing the Lord's song
>   in a foreign land?   (Psalm 137:1-4)

That they learned to sing the Lord's song in the land of exile, that they learned the great truth that the Lord was with them, was due in large measure to the prophet who taught them to sing.

Several scholars have noted the large number of parallels between Ezekiel's prophecy and the book of Leviticus.[5] In my estimation, much of this discussion is now obsolete, since the archaeological discoveries of the past fifty years have certainly made it unnecessary to give the institution of priestly ritual a late date. If we accept an essentially Aaronic (or Mosaic) origin for the book of Leviticus, and the tradi-

---

[5] The picture is sometimes obscured to the layman due to the fact that the scholars insist on talking about "H" (or "the Holiness Code," Leviticus 17-26) and "P" (or "the Priestly Code," which may be roughly approximated to the rest of Leviticus for our present purpose). To make the matter still more difficult, scholars are not at all agreed upon the date they assign to the final writing of Ezekiel, nor to the exact relationship between H and P and the editorial work on Ezekiel.

tional view of sixth century authorship of Ezekiel,[6] we get the following picture, which in my opinion is self-consistent and compatible with
the known facts.

Ezekiel was a priest, schooled in the priestly office, therefore
thoroughly familiar with the Levitical legislation. He used its phrase-
ology often.[7] Now, what was the purpose of the Levitical legislation?
It was to establish the people of Israel as a "peculiar people." Repeatedly
the expression is used, "you shall be holy." The basic idea in the word
"holy" is *separation*. It comes to have an ethical meaning—and we
certainly lose the great purpose behind the Law if we lose sight of the
ethical significance. "You shall be holy; for I the Lord your God am
holy" (Leviticus 19:2), does not mean that God is aloof from the sinful
world; it means that He is morally straight or "righteous." A careful
reading of the Levitical laws should make that clear. But in protecting
the ethical connotation, let us not lose the basic idea of separation. These
people were about to go into the land of the Canaanites, the land of
gross idolatry and gross sin. They were to be a peculiar people, set
apart from the Canaanites by peculiar rituals, peculiar garb, peculiar
dietary laws, particularly by the Sabbaths, all designed to mark out
the separation. Their sin, as proclaimed by all the prophets—and
Ezekiel is certainly no exception!—had been due to the loss of this
sense of separation and the concomitant loss of holiness. Now, as they
are about to go into the land of Babylonia (in fulfillment of Leviticus
26:14-45, we might note) where they might easily be swallowed up
forever, it is necessary for God to remind them once more of His purpose for them. Ezekiel is His servant, and the Levitical Law is at the
heart of his message. These people must be reminded that they belong
to the Lord. Notice how many times Ezekiel echoes the familiar words
of Leviticus, "I am the Lord."

We have already given some indication of the days in which Ezekiel
lived. For the first thirty-five years of his life he was contemporary with
Jeremiah. The three great powers (today, I suppose, we would call
them "the Big Three"), Egypt, Assyria, and Babylonia, were going

[6] This latter point is ably defended by C. G. Howie, *The Date and Composi-
tion of Ezekiel* (Philadelphia: Society of Biblical Literature, 1950), note pp. 100-
102.

[7] "The parallels with Lev. 26:3ff. are peculiarly numerous and striking, including several expressions not occurring elsewhere in the Old Testament," says S. R.
Driver, *An Introduction to the Literature of the Old Testament* (9th ed., Edin-
burgh: T. & T. Clark, 1913), p. 147, and then he lists 27 of these expressions.

through a time of transition. Egypt had temporarily risen to strength after a few centuries of impotence. Assyria was on the way out. Babylon was rising to the top—but would not stay there long. The smaller nations were feeling growing pains and small wars were breaking out in many places. How much like our own day it was! About 626 B.C. the Scythians had broken through from the north, and had moved toward Egypt. We do not know much about them—they are not mentioned by name in the Old Testament—other than the fact that they came from the region around the Black Sea.[8] Probably they are the background for the figure used in the prophets, especially Jeremiah, Ezekiel, and Zephaniah, of the scourge to come from the north. I do not mean to say that the Scythians fulfill these prophecies; I simply mean that such an invasion of a hitherto-unknown people, being fresh in the minds of the people of Israel, would be an apt figure to drive home the truth of a prophecy of future trouble out of the north.

It has been suggested that this Scythian invasion may have been the event that triggered the reform in the days of Josiah five years later, the year Ezekiel was born. It is possible that Josiah was deeply impressed by his escape from some unknown fate when the Scythians were bribed by Pharaoh Psamtik to go back home. God uses various ways of touching the hearts of men. However, splendid as the reform of Josiah was, it apparently had no deep roots in the lives of the people. Soon they were paying Egypt for protection—with an Egyptian puppet on the throne; then they were paying Babylonia for protection—with a Babylonian puppet on the throne. And hardly anyone remembered that their best protection was the Lord of hosts; and He should be on the throne. Ezekiel reminded them.

Ezekiel's message can be divided into three main sections, covering the Fall of Jerusalem (chapters 1—24), the Judgment upon the Nations (chapters 25—32), and the Restoration of the City (chapters 33—48). The first section can be further subdivided into three parts, or three "cycles of threats."[9] It is as though God has drawn up a bill of particulars setting forth the reasons for the judgment that is to fall, and that Ezekiel is commissioned to read the horrible details.

---

[8] Recently an advocate of the British-Israel theory was trying to convince me that the Scythians (the Saxons, he pointed out, with some fanciful etymological equations) were the "Lost Tribes." When I asked him how they managed to be threatening Egypt less than a hundred years after they had been taken into captivity, he seemed to be completely ignorant of this detail of history.

[9] This expression I have taken from *A Catholic Commentary on Holy Scripture*, p. 602.

The first "cycle of threats" (chapters 1—11) begins with the mysterious visions of chapter one. Living creatures with four faces and wheels within wheels: someone has suggested that they represent second causes, both living and inorganic; but over them was a throne and over the throne One like us in form. He is the Prime Mover, all else are second causes. Historians try to explain the rise and decline of nations; the prophet knows that it is God in the last analysis who is accomplishing His will.

It is an indication of the spiritual level of our own day, I think, that we fail to understand that Israel's worst sin was the sin of idolatry, apostasy, turning from the true God. "What is so bad about that?" we ask. We would be much more impressed if God had specified a list of crimes: gas chambers, concentration camps, broken treaties, the use of poison gas or flame throwers or nuclear weapons; child marriage, polygamy, sweat shops, slave labor; gluttony and drunkenness, and the like. Some of the prophets do enumerate such social sins—and they are more frequently quoted and better understood today. But Israel's worst sin was turning from God! Until we understand the awful depth of that sin, we ourselves are under condemnation; for until we thoroughly believe that God is supreme in this universe and act upon that faith, we have denied to Him the honor that is His right and we have rebelled against His authority.

Ezekiel saw the glory of God move from the cherubim in the Holy Place to the threshold (9:3), and then from the threshold to the east gate (10:19), and then from the midst of the city to the mountain on the east side (the Mount of Olives) (11:23). The glory of the Lord's presence that had filled the house when Solomon dedicated it (II Chronicles 5:13-14) had departed, because Solomon and his successors had failed to heed the Lord's warning: "If you turn aside and forsake my statutes and my commandments which I have set before you, and go and serve other gods and worship them, then I will pluck you up from the land which I have given you; and this house, which I have consecrated for my name, I will cast out of my sight . . ." (II Chronicles 7:19-22).

There was mercy there, too, for God had put a mark on the foreheads of the men who were truly penitent (Ezekiel 9:4), and the Lord's ministers of judgment spared those who were marked (cf. Revelation 7:3; 14:1).

Ezekiel was appalled by the threat, and he cried out, "Ah Lord God! wilt thou make a full end of the remnant of Israel?" Then God told him of the regathering of the exiles, of the new heart of flesh, and added "they shall be my people, and I will be their God" (11:13-20).

The second "cycle of threats" (chapters 12—19) begins by singling out the false prophets and prophetesses, and laying upon them the burden of guilt for misleading the people (chapter 13). God names the sins, and says that even if the three most righteous men of old were in the city (it reminds us of how Abraham had pled for the sparing of Sodom for Lot's sake), they could only succeed in sparing themselves (14:14). Then God rehearses the history of Israel in a touching story (chapter 16).

This people was like an unwanted girl, cast out to die when God found her and took her. He cared for her in the days of her childhood, and when she came to maturity He "spread his skirt" over her (remember Ruth and Boaz?), He married her, He made her a beautiful queen, famous throughout the world. Then this wife proved unfaithful. With the Egyptians, the Assyrians, and the Babylonians (or Chaldeans), she played the harlot. Her sins were many, and they were deep. Yet, God would remember His covenant with her in the days of her youth, and the time would come, He told her, when she would "remember and be confounded, and never open your mouth again because of your shame, when I forgive you all that you have done" (16:63). That is the greatest love theme of all time—the love of God for His faithless and sinful people.

The idea that personal responsibility was lost in corporate existence must be set straight. "What do you mean by repeating this proverb concerning the land of Israel, 'The fathers have eaten sour grapes, and the children's teeth are set on edge'?" (Ezekiel 18:2). "Behold, all souls are mine," says God; "the soul of the father as well as the soul of the son is mine: the soul that sins shall die" (18:4). And God makes it clear and simple that each man must stand on his own feet. Spiritual life is a matter of personal responsibility before God. Church membership does not save, any more than does physical Israelite lineage; each man stands before God on the basis of his own relationship to God (18:20). But over and above this truth is the greater truth: *God does not take pleasure in the death of the wicked!* (18:23). "Why will you die, O house of Israel? For I have no pleasure in the death of anyone, says the Lord God; *so turn, and live*" (18:31-32).

In the third cycle of threats, God reminds them of the statutes and ordinances which they have failed to observe, especially the Sabbaths (20:12). We get an insight into the heart of God when He remarks, "I will be king over you" (20:33). He promises to bring them out from the countries where they have been scattered: "And you shall know that I am the Lord, when I deal with you for my name's sake, not according to your evil ways, nor according to your corrupt doings, O house of Israel, says the Lord God" (20:44).

Then, on the very day that Jerusalem was taken, God took away the delight of Ezekiel's eyes, his beloved wife—and told him that he could not even express his grief in proper mourning. This was to be a sign to the people (24:24).

We pass over the judgments upon the nations (chapters 25—32) with the observation that nations used by God as instruments of His judgment do not themselves escape judgment. Judgment begins at the house of the Lord and with the elders of His people (Ezekiel 9:6); but it does not stop until all have been judged. The picture of the judgment of Tyre especially fascinates us (chapters 26—28): first, because it is the finest extant picture of the maritime mercantile life of the Ancient Middle East; but especially because it is so markedly similar to the judgment upon Babylon in Revelation 18. Likewise, the picture of hell is striking, with the roll call of those who are there (Ezekiel 32:18-32). We would probably like to add a few more recent nations to the list!

With chapter 33, and the news that the city has fallen, God repeats the charge to Ezekiel and His desire that men repent and turn to Him. Now the message turns to hope and assurance.

False shepherds who have been interested only in their own security have let the nation get into this mess. God not only says, "I am against the shepherds; and I will require my sheep at their hand"; He goes on to say, "I myself will search for my sheep . . . I myself will be the shepherd of my sheep." And He promises to restore the line of David (34:10-23). How can anyone miss this amazing prophecy? How can anyone think that it is just another son of David, or David himself come back from the dead, of whom Ezekiel speaks? No more human shepherds, says God. I myself. "If David thus calls him Lord, how is he his son?" (Matthew 22:45). "And you are my sheep, the sheep of my pasture, and I am your God, says the Lord God" (Ezekiel 34:31). "I am the good shepherd; I know my own and my own know me," says the Lord Jesus Christ (John 10:14).

Why does God restore His people? Is it because of some good that is in them? some intrinsic worth? "It is not for your sake, O house of Israel, that I am about to act, but for the sake of my holy name . . . I will take you . . . gather you . . . bring you. . . . I will sprinkle clean water upon you. . . . A new heart I will give you. . . . I will put my spirit within you. . . . It is not for your sake that I will act, says the Lord God; let that be known to you" (36:22-32). This is what theologians call "grace"—undeserved love. "God shows his love for us in that while we were yet sinners Christ died for us" (Romans 5:8).

Is Ezekiel now talking of the church? Is the church the fulfillment of God's promises to Israel? Though many will disagree, I must say that I do not think so. The thirty-seventh chapter of Ezekiel is talking about Israel (37:11, 19). The same Israel that was scattered and dead, like dead bones in a very dry valley: this is the Israel that God revives. The same two sticks that were Joseph and Judah in captivity are united by God to be one stick. Only the most forced exegesis can get rid of the clear teaching of this passage; and only the most forced exegesis can get rid of the same clear teaching in Romans 11.

But the prophet's eye seems to confuse the near and the distant.[10] He sees the restored Israel in the land at the same time as he sees the everlasting Davidic prince (Ezekiel 37:25). God has not let him see clearly the interval which our Lord called "the times of the Gentiles" (Luke 21:24).

Charles Erdman has pointed out that "Ezekiel is absolutely unique among all the Old Testament prophets in predicting another invasion of their land after the people of Israel have been restored and are dwelling in peace and security under the will of their Good Shepherd."[11] The language of the thirty-eighth chapter of Ezekiel is so clearly similar to the language of the Book of Revelation, particularly portions of the nineteenth and twentieth chapters, that I am forced to consider them together when I am interpreting either book. It therefore seems to me that Ezekiel is speaking of a time, after the glorious messianic promises have begun to be fulfilled, when the godless forces of the world shall make one last effort against the people of God in the land of promise.

[10] This is sometimes called "prophetic foreshortening," or "prophetic perspective." Catholic scholars may refer to it as "compenetration" resulting in a lack of chronological perspective. Its existence in Scripture is responsible for the fact that Jesus' contemporaries were looking for elements of the Second Advent (as we know it) mixed with the elements of the First Advent.

[11] The Book of Ezekiel, p. 117.

And that time, God Himself will enter the battle and bring to an end such human madness (Ezekiel 38:19-23).

There is little else I would say. Just as the seer of Patmos saw the New Jerusalem, so Ezekiel was granted the vision. I am not convinced that we should attempt to press all the physical details in either case, for God's word is concerned with the souls of men rather than with architecture or real estate. Imagery and symbolism may turn out to be closer to the real than we had thought, and if so, we have not lost a thing. But if we miss the spiritual truth behind the image, then we have lost all. The size of the New Jerusalem is less important than the kind of people who are in it. It is not big enough for godless men (Revelation 21:8). Whether the streets are of real gold is less important than the fact that the river of life flows through the city, with healing for the nations growing on its banks (22:2). Whether there was a temple or not (John did not see it), is less important than the fact that its temple is the Lord God Almighty and the Lamb (21:22).

So it is with Ezekiel's vision. The height of the walls is not great enough for either defense or display (Ezekiel 40:5); but it serves to remind us that only holiness can get in (43:12). Whether the temple will be rebuilt to Ezekiel's dimensions, I do not know (it is interesting to remember that Zerubbabel did not attempt it); what matters is that Ezekiel saw the glory of the Lord returning by the eastern gate, and filling the temple (43:5). Whether an actual river will flow from Jerusalem into the Ghôr to sweeten the waters of the Dead Sea, I cannot say with great conviction; but I am sure of this: Jerusalem will be the source of life and health and abundance (47:10-12). "But how," someone will ask, "can you be so sure of this, if you are not sure about these other matters?" The reason is simple: "the name of the city henceforth shall be, The Lord is there" (48:35).

The Lord is there, but will you be there? Israel's story is given to us as a lesson. As God spared not Israel, but required of her double for all her sins, so will He not spare any who have turned from Him. But why will you die? God has no pleasure in the death of the wicked; all He wants is the recognition that He is supreme, and submission to His will. You give this to human rulers; why will you not give it to the Lord of heaven and earth?

CHAPTER XVII

Daniel

DANIEL's book is dark and mysterious, and there are many who do not know it, and some who do not like it, and some do not understand it. Whether the Book of Daniel is interesting to you or not, the man whose name it carries is an interesting character and an important one.

Daniel was from the princely line of Judah and he was carried into captivity from Jerusalem to Babylon in the first captivity under Nebuchadnezzar[1] (605 B.C.). According to tradition, he was about twelve or fifteen at the time. When he got to the city of Babylon, he was included in a group which was chosen to be trained as statesmen. The king commanded his chief eunuch "to bring some of the people of Israel, both of the royal family and of the nobility, youths without blemish, handsome and skillful in all wisdom, endowed with knowledge, understanding, learning, and competent to serve in the king's palace, and to teach them the letters and language of the Chaldeans"[2] (1:3-4). They were to be educated for three years and at the end of that time they were to stand before the king. In other words, the king saw here a group of young men that he could use in his court: and Daniel was one of them. Now if this group was taken captive in 605 B.C., and if Daniel was still serving when the empire fell to Cyrus in 539 B.C., you can readily see that Daniel served in that court for more than sixty years.

In the modern Hebrew Bible, Daniel's book is not listed among the "Prophets," but rather among the "Writings." This has led some to object to any reference to the book as a "prophecy." Perhaps it will help us to understand something of the man as well as something of his book, if we take time to discuss this point. In the story of Samuel we came across the statement, "he who is now called a prophet was for-

[1] The form Nebuchadnezzar is used in this chapter because it is the form used in Daniel; see note 1 on page 147, above.

[2] "Chaldeans" is a name used for the Neo-Babylonian empire, probably arising from the fact that the dominant race in the empire was from Chaldea (southern Babylonia). In Herodotus the name becomes synonymous with the priests of Marduk (or Bel).

merly called a seer" (I Samuel 9:9). There were, then, two terms, "prophet" and "seer."[3] The terms are used somewhat interchangeably, which leads to further confusion. But as I understand them, the word "prophet" stresses the idea that God has spoken that which is being delivered, whereas the word "seer" stresses the idea that God has given a revelation in a dream or vision. Prophets could be seers, as the example of Samuel clearly proves; and prophets, as we know from Amos and Ezekiel and others, could receive their message from visions. When the vision was given by the Lord as the basis for a message to the people Israel, the seer was acting as a prophet. But—and here, I think, is the important point to remember when we are studying Daniel —when the vision was not the basis for a message to Israel, then the seer was not acting as a prophet.[4] So far as I can discover, Daniel does not claim that God spoke to him; he received his revelations in the forms of dreams and visions. And so far as I can discover, Daniel does not address the people Israel. He never uses the words, "Thus said the Lord."

There is another fact that has to be brought into this discussion. Daniel's ministry seems to have been not to the people of Israel immediately (although ultimately it was, because the message was written in a book and sealed up until the proper time), but to the Gentile kings under whom he was serving. It makes him unique among the Old Testament characters, that his ministry was immediately directed not toward the chosen people but toward that nation which held the chosen people in captivity.[5] While they were in exile God had a message for the ones who were holding them, and Daniel was the man who gave them that message.

He lived in Jerusalem, as we have already said, when Nebuchadnezzar carried the first group into captivity. God had spoken through the prophets to His people; He had chastised them because of their unbelief and their apostasy, and had threatened to punish them, but they

[3] Actually there are three terms, for two Hebrew words, rô'êh and hôzêh, are translated "seer"; as far as I can determine, these two were completely synonymous.

[4] Some scholars see a difference between the "prophetic office" and the "prophetic gift"; Daniel, they tell us, had the latter, but not the former. Cf. E. J. Young, The Prophecy of Daniel (Grand Rapids: Wm. B. Eerdmans Publishing Co., 1949), pp. 20-21.

[5] The contrast between Ezekiel and Daniel has often been pointed out: Ezekiel was the prophet of the Lord to the Jews in exile; Daniel was the Lord's servant in the court of the Gentile power that held the Jews captive.

had not repented. The long-awaited punishment of God fell at last on the Southern Kingdom; and it came in three stages, as though God were loath to move all the way through with this thing. He took away their king and the vessels from the temple in 605; He struck them again with another wave of punishment about 597; and finally in 586 the city was wiped out entirely, and the temple was burned.

Nebuchadnezzar, the king of Babylon from 605 to 562, whose reign is described as one of the longest and most brilliant in human history, was the man used by God to take the Southern Kingdom into captivity. The Neo-Babylonian empire had come into being only a few years before that; Nineveh, the capital of Assyria, fell in 612 B.C. The collapse of Assyria had come about not because Babylonia was so strong but because they had united with a couple of other kingdoms and, united they were able to overthrow this great Assyrian empire. But what happens when a coalition of powers overthrows a powerful enemy? Those who unite with you for the destruction of your common foe—as we have had occasion to learn since 1945—may turn against you as soon as the enemy has been defeated. The Babylonian empire was destined to be short-lived: it had too many enemies.

Nebuchadnezzar built Babylon. I visited it several years ago and found nothing but a heap of mounds, as the prophet Ezekiel said it was going to be: a dwelling place of jackals. But I could see the remains of the ancient city in the ruins, far and wide, everywhere I looked. The guide would say, "You see that big mound over there? Well, that was the tower of Marduk." And looking the other way he would say, "That is all that remains of the city gate." There were great walls around Babylon. According to Herodotus, the Greek historian who lived about a century later, the city was built like a huge square, with walls about fourteen miles long on each side (a later historian agrees that the city was fourteen miles long, but makes the circumference only forty-two miles), fifty great cubits wide (about eighty-four feet), and two hundred great cubits high (about 333 feet). Herodotus further tells us that first a wide and deep moat had been dug, the earth of which had been used to make bricks for the wall, and then the moat had been filled with water from the river. The river itself flowed through the midst of the city. On top of the wall were two rows of buildings, one at each edge, and between them was a place wide enough to drive four-horse chariots. There were one hundred bronze gates in the wall.[6]

Even if we allow for considerable exaggeration, the picture that

[6] Herodotus, Book I, § 178.

Herodotus gives is impressive. But if you could walk around the ruins and see the unusually large buildings, if you could look at the remains of the famous Ishtar Gate (the most beautiful part, the blue-glazed tile façade, was taken to Berlin by the excavator, Koldewey), if you could walk the length of the walls for even the part that has been discovered, you would wonder whether Herodotus *has* exaggerated.[7] But this is only part of the story.

Nebuchadnezzar had a wife who came from the mountainous country of Persia, and she longed for mountains; so he built for her what have been known as the hanging gardens, one of the seven wonders of the ancient world. Actually they were not hanging gardens, but artificial mountains constructed in the city and planted over with trees, so that his queen, looking out at them, would have a memory of the mountains she had left behind when she moved to that monotonously flat land. He also built a reservoir at Sippara which, we are told, had a circumference of 160 miles, and was 180 feet deep, to supply the country with water for its agriculture. He built canals between the Euphrates and the Tigris so that the country could be irrigated. And he built a dock system down on the Persian Gulf. A tremendous king! Imagine being advisor to a king like that!

Nebuchadnezzar had a dream, and he called in the court magicians and wise men. Notice the way he put the problem to his wise men: You tell me what I dreamed and what it means. Anyone could make up an interpretation of a dream; only a truly wise man could tell him what he had dreamed. And of course, they were unable to do what he commanded. Then Daniel was brought in and the same request was made of him: "Are you able to make known to me the dream that I have seen and its interpretation?" Daniel replied frankly, "No wise men . . . can show to the king the mystery which the king has asked, but there is a God in heaven who reveals mysteries . . ." (2:26-28), and he gave the interpretation. Nebuchadnezzar had dreamed of an image with four parts: the first of these four parts was the Babylonian empire; following that would be three successive empires, and at last the image was struck with a stone which is not cut by human hands,

---

[7] For splendid photographs of reconstructions of the tower of Marduk, the Ishtar Gate, and Procession Street with the Hanging Gardens, see H. Schmökel, *Ur, Assur und Babylon* (in *Grosse Kulturen der Frühzeit*; Stuttgart: Gustav Kilpper Verlag, 1955), plates 114-115. Color plates of a large enamelled-brick lion from the Procession Street and of the elaborately decorated wall of the throne-room can be found in H. Schäffer und W. Andrae, *Die Kunst des alten Orients* (Berlin: Propyläen-Verlag, 1925), plates XXIX-XXX.

and the whole thing was smashed; but the stone that had smashed it became a great mountain. We will talk about the interpretation of it later.

Of course the king was greatly impressed with Daniel's ability to describe and interpret this vision, and he gave him honors and gifts, and a place of prominence (2:46-48).

In the fourth chapter Nebuchadnezzar has another dream, and again Daniel has to interpret. The dream is of a tree which had grown very large, and then was cut down, stripped of its branches and its leaves, its fruit was scattered, and only the stump was left. Daniel interprets it to mean that the king was to be visited with severe punishment, "till you know that the Most High rules the kingdom of men and gives it to whom he will" (4:24-27).

The outcome of it is described at the end of the chapter. The king was walking along the roof of the royal palace, looking at this immense city with its great gates, its great walls, its hanging gardens, and all the rest of it, and he said, in a moment of pride: "Is not this great Babylon which I have built by my mighty power?" And there came a voice from heaven, "O King Nebuchadnezzar, to you it is spoken, the kingdom has departed from you. . . ." The king became subject to a disease known as lycanthropy, in which he imagined himself to be a beast; he went out and ate grass in the field like an ox, and he lost the right of his kingdom for seven years. At the end of that time he came to realize that his dominion was only his because God had given it to him, and that God's dominion is an everlasting dominion.

Two lesser kings succeeded him, and then Nabonidus came to the throne. Nabonidus was a rather strange character; he apparently was more interested in vacations than in being king. He spent almost all of his reign, according to his royal letters, in an oasis out in the desert named Tema. He put his son Belshazzar on the throne as co-regent; in the book of Daniel he is called King, although in the letters he is simply called the king's first son. The king was actually absent from the throne, though, out there in the desert halfway to Egypt, and the son had all of the responsibilities of the kingdom; it was his lot to reign for the closing days of the Babylonian empire and to see it collapse before the Persian thrust.[8]

[8] A thorough discussion of this whole problem will be found in R. P. Dougherty, *Nabonidus and Belshazzar* (*Yale Oriental Series;* New Haven: Yale University Press, 1929), 216 pp.

There is not a great deal to be told about either Belshazzar or Nabonidus. Their days were not splendid days; they were days when the force of the other kingdoms which had united with Babylonia against Assyria was turned against their former ally. If it had been glorious to be advisor to the king in the days of Nebuchadnezzar, I suppose it must have been disappointing to be his advisor in the days that followed when it was only a matter of time before the kingdom collapsed. It must have been especially bitter to see how little interest the king took in the kingdom. He was warned repeatedly for three years that the Persians were advancing, but he did nothing about it. At last he rushed into the city to try to save what little he could, but it was too late.[9]

In the days of Belshazzar, Daniel dreamed a dream: a dream of four beasts, and it should be placed beside the dream of Nebuchadnezzar of the four-part image, for both of these dreams teach the same general lesson. The story, you will note, is not told in chronological order. Chapter 5 tells of the end of Belshazzar's reign; chapter 6, the beginning of the Persian reign; and chapter 7 takes us back to the days of Belshazzar, prior to the end of his kingdom. I think we should also note that chapter 7 begins the second half of Daniel, and that its form is different from that of the first half: the second half consists of dreams and visions which Daniel had and which he wrote down in a book— a book "shut up and sealed until the time of the end." The four beasts of Daniel's dreams represented "four kings who shall arise out of the earth" (7:17). I shall come back to them a bit later. The fact of primary significance is expressed in the verse that follows: "But the saints of the Most High shall receive the kingdom, and possess the kingdom, for ever and ever." The kingdoms of this world are great and terrible. God's people know that, especially when they come under the heel of these kingdoms. But the kingdoms of this world are not eternal. The dominion that is an everlasting dominion, and the kingdom that shall not be destroyed belongs to the One whom Daniel saw coming with the clouds of heaven, One like a son of man (7:13-14).

The Babylonian empire had been the instrument in God's hands to punish faithless Israel. But it was not going to last forever. Its end was

---

[9] It is perhaps unfair to suggest that it was only pleasure that attracted Nabonidus to Tema. Dougherty thinks that it may have had strategic value, and that Nabonidus was seeking allies against Persia. But prolonged absence (five years, possibly nine) hardly seems necessary for such a purpose.

at hand. For that, we go back to the fifth chapter. Belshazzar made a great feast for a thousand of his lords. God had tried to make Nebuchadnezzar understand that he was on the throne of Babylon and the Babylonian empire was strong only because God had allowed it. He had allowed it as a means of punishment against His people Israel. The punishment that fell upon Nebuchadnezzar was due to the fact that he had failed to recognize that he was king only under God. Belshazzar went a step further than Nebuchadnezzar: he not only forgot that he was on the throne by virtue of God's will, but he dared to take the golden vessels that had been captured by Nebuchadnezzar in Jerusalem, the sacred vessels that had been used only in the worship of Jehovah in the temple—he dared to take these and use them as drinking vessels for his drunken party. "Immediately the fingers of a man's hand appeared and wrote on the plaster of the wall of the king's palace, opposite the lampstand; and the king saw the hand as it wrote. Then the king's color changed, and his thoughts alarmed him; his limbs gave way, and his knees knocked together. The king cried aloud to bring in the enchanters, the Chaldeans, and the astrologers . . ." (5:5-6), to find out what the hand had written. None of them was able to interpret it.

The queen remembered that there was a Jew at that court who could interpret dreams; the king brought in Daniel and said, "if you can read the writing and make known to me its interpretation, you shall be clothed with purple, and have a chain of gold about your neck, and shall be the third ruler in the kingdom" (5:14-16).[10]

Daniel told him to keep his gifts, but ". . . nevertheless I will read the writing"; and he read the four words: "MENE, MENE, TEKEL and PARSIN." Now those are quite common words, and we may well ask, Why could the king not understand them? There are several possible reasons. The words are Aramaic, and the king was Babylonian—although we know that Aramaic was widely used as a diplomatic language just following that period, and we suppose some of the men of the court could speak it. Aramaic however is written with just the consonants, and the same group of consonants may be read two or three

[10] For years they wondered why Belshazzar, who was named as king in this book, would make Daniel *third* in the kingdom; why not make him second? It is only since we have learned that Nabonidus was the true king and that Belshazzar his son was reigning in his place as second in the kingdom that we have understood why Daniel could only be named third. Belshazzar could not name him second, because that would have put him in the place of Belshazzar himself.

ways. For example, these words could be read as sums of money: Mina, Tekel (Shekel), and Fractions (Half-shekels). Now suppose suddenly you saw the words on the wall before you, "Dollar, dollar, dime, and nickels"—what would you understand by them? The wise men may have recognized the words; but they were unable to read (understand) or interpret them. Or again, the words could be read as forms of common verbs: Weighed, numbered, divisions. But what did that mean? Daniel chided the king for his pride and presumption, and then interpreted the words: "God has numbered the days of your kingdom and brought it to an end . . . you have been weighed in the balances and found wanting . . . your kingdom is divided and given to the Medes and Persians" (5:26-28). That very night, while the king feasted in confidence that his city could not be taken in twenty years, the Persian troops succeeded in diverting the river into the moats around the city, marched in by the river-bed, and took Babylon "without firing a shot."[11] Belshazzar was killed; how, we do not know.

The king of the Persian empire was Cyrus, but he himself did not enter the city of Babylon that night; his minister, one of his governors named Darius or Gobyrus (Ugbaru), led the capture. Cyrus was proud of the fact that when he took a country he liberated his prisoners, and he writes in his annals that he looked upon himself as a liberator of the gods. When they captured a country, it was the custom to take the gods from the temples and bring them to the victor's country as proof that the dominion over the conquered country extended even to its gods. Cyrus says that he sent these gods back to their homes. But above all, he sent the Israelites home; their captivity was over.

Now let us set the message of Daniel against his day, and see what it says to us. His message came when Israel was in captivity. But more than that, it came at the time when a world came to its end. The night that the Persian forces turned aside the Euphrates and marched into Babylon, that night the dominion of the world passed from East to West. Up until that moment, the great empires of the world had been Oriental empires. From that moment until this present day, the empires of the world have been Indo-European, non-Semitic empires; Persian, Greek, Roman, British.

[11] The Nabonidus Chronicle says simply, "On the sixteenth day Ugbaru the governor of Gutium and the troops of Cyrus without fighting entered Babylon"; and Cyrus says, "Without any battle he [i.e. Marduk] made him [Cyrus] enter his town Babylon, sparing Babylon any calamity." The documents may be seen in Dougherty, *Nabonidus and Belshazzar*, pp. 170, 176.

But worlds come to an end slowly. And people who live in the end of an age probably have no idea at all that epochal events are occurring. That is why the prophet of God is essential for interpretation. Daniel's interpretations of the image of four parts and the four beasts are important because they help us understand what was taking place in the world. Four successive world empires came into existence in this world. The first was the Neo-Babylonian Empire of Nebuchadnezzar. That the interpretation must begin here is clearly indicated, for Daniel said to Nebuchadnezzar, "You are the head of gold." The second was the Persian Empire under Cyrus, the Achaemenian dynasty. The third was the Macedonian Empire under Alexander the Great, and the fourth the Roman Empire.[12] Daniel says that in the day of the fourth kingdom a stone that had not been fashioned by human power smashed the image. What is he saying? He is saying that the world empires, the empires established by the hands of Nebuchadnezzar and Cyrus and Alexander and the Caesars, are only here for a limited time. They are tolerated by God. God has them here for a purpose. But they shall not last forever.

There is a greater kingdom to come: "In the days of those kings the God of heaven will set up a kingdom which shall never be destroyed, nor shall its sovereignty be left to another people. It shall break in pieces all these [previous] kingdoms and bring them to an end, and it shall stand forever" (Daniel 2:44-45). And again, "I saw in the night visions, and behold, with the clouds of heaven there came one like a son of man, and he came to the Ancient of Days and was presented before him. And to him was given dominion and glory and kingdom, that all peoples, nations, and languages should serve him; his dominion is an everlasting dominion, which shall not pass away, and his kingdom one that shall not be destroyed" (7:12-14).

You and I are living in the day of the end of the kingdoms, as Daniel prophesied. I am not a fanatic; I am not saying the end of the

---

[12] Another school of interpretation holds: (1) Neo-Babylonian, (2) Medes, (3) Persians, (4) Greek. But this is impossible, for the Medes and the Persians were never two great empires. Therefore a third school is growing that interprets: (1) Neo-Babylonian, (2) Medo-Persian, (3) Macedonian (Alexander), (4) the successors of Alexander (Seleucids and Ptolemies). The main argument is that the fourth empire is destroyed before the messianic kingdom is established (Daniel 7:11-13). But this argument fails when the messianic kingdom is viewed in its first- and second-advent aspects. The fact remains: it was in the fourth kingdom that the messianic kingdom arose—and that was in the Roman Empire!

world is coming tomorrow, or the day after tomorrow. I am simply saying that we have already gone through the four parts of the image of the second chapter and four beasts of the seventh chapter; therefore certainly we are living in the end of the days of this image. We are living in the days when the One like the Son of Man has come, and when the kingdom which was not made with human hands has come and struck the kingdoms of the world; and we have this message: that *the kingdoms of this world cannot stand, but the Kingdom of God is forever.* In a day when armies seem to be on the march again and when we are afraid to read tomorrow's headlines for fear they will say that another war has broken out, we can thank God that we belong to a Kingdom which has no end.

CHAPTER XVIII

Ezra

Ezra was not a prophet but a priest and a scribe. The kingdom was over, at least for the moment, hence the prophetic voice was stilled. Haggai had been sent to encourage the people to rebuild the temple; the temple, Zerubbabel, and Joshua, in his prophecy are all strongly typical of the Messiah to come. Zechariah had carried on the typology of Zerubbabel, and then abandoned it to speak directly of the Messiah and His coming. Malachi had been sent to answer the questions that Jews were asking: questions about the love and justice of God; and to tell them of the coming judgment that is an inevitable part of justice, and the coming possession that is an inevitable result of love. Then God was silent. But the Law and the Prophets were still there (remember how Jesus turned aside the request for a convincing sign with the statement, "They have Moses and the prophets; let them hear them"? Luke 16:29), and men needed only to be taught the Scriptures. Hence, in the providence of God, the priesthood, and especially the office of the scribe, came into prominence.

Ezra is traditionally looked upon as the first of the scribes, and in a sense he might be looked upon as the founder of Judaism. What would have happened to Judaism if it had not been for Ezra and the men of the Great Synagogue?[1] And, humanly speaking, how could Christianity have gotten started in the world if there had not been the Scriptures preserved and studied by the scribes, and the Pharisees with their meticulous zeal to keep the Law, and the seed of David of which the Christ was born according to the flesh? So in a very special way Ezra is the link between the old and the new. Coming at the time when the Old Testament was complete,[2] he stands in a unique place with

[1] See G. F. Moore, *Judaism* (Cambridge, Mass.: Harvard University Press, 1927), Vol. I, 29-47, for an authoritative discussion of Ezra, the Great Synagogue, and the scribes.

[2] It is obvious that I reject the idea of late post-Exilic writings in the Old Testament. One of the strong arguments against this idea, it seems to me, is the lack of *creative* writing in the last pre-Christian centuries. It was the nature of the

reference to Judaism and to Christianity. He is a fitting personality, I believe, to bring to a close our series of studies.

Ezra was born and raised in Babylonia in the days of the captivity. He traces his lineage to Aaron through Zadok and Phinehas (Ezra 7:2, 4). It would indeed be difficult to prove that these men contributed physically to Ezra's heritage at such great distance; but it is not unreasonable to say that they contributed psychologically. The very fact that he was proud to trace his line back to them may suggest that he desired to have something in common with them, that, even though it may have been subconsciously, he tried to be like them.

Zadok was one of the priests who went with the leaders of the tribes of Israel to David when he was at Hebron, to offer to him the kingship and to turn the kingdom from Saul to David. Zadok stayed with David through all the turbulent episodes of his career. At the end, when there was an abortive attempt to get the succession away from David's favorite son Solomon, when Abiathar the priest cast in his lot with the plot of Joab, Zadok remained loyal to David and backed Solomon. For this, his line, rather than the line of Abiathar, was established in the priestly succession (see I Kings 1—2). Zadok was the name henceforth that suggested loyalty to the Davidic line.[3]

Phinehas, whom Ezra also mentions, takes our thoughts back to the time of Moses and his elder brother Aaron and the sin of the Israelites at Baal-peor. The sin is described in the twenty-fifth chapter of Numbers. The Israelites were joining with the Moabites in the worship of Baal, and "the anger of the Lord was kindled against Israel." One of the Israelites took one of the Midianite women in the sight of Moses and in the sight of the whole congregation of the people of Israel, to commit with her the abomination which was called "worship" of the god of Baal, and Phinehas took his spear and thrust it through the man and the woman in the act of sin. A plague had come upon the people

---

scribes and the great teachers to be *interpretative*. Other writings are *imitative*. But where are the creative writers, other than in the Scriptures? These cannot be used to support a circular argument.

[3] It is interesting to note that the Sadducees, in the formative days when they took (or received) their name, were called Zadokites (of which Sadducees is a corruption). Some years later, in a reform movement, the group that split off called themselves "the true sons of Zadok." This group finally located at the place we know as Qumran, and gave us the materials we call "The Dead Sea Scrolls." Reasons for some of the statements I have made here, together with a sketch of the historical development, can be found in my volume, *Amazing Dead Sea Scrolls* (Chicago: The Moody Press, 1956), pp. 195-200, 222-224.

of Israel as punishment for sin they were committing; but the plague was stayed. "And the Lord said to Moses, "Phinehas the son of Eleazar, son of Aaron the priest, has turned back my wrath from the people of Israel [and I think this is an amazing statement] in that he was jealous with my jealousy among them, so that I did not consume the people of Israel in my jealousy" (Numbers 25:10-11). Phinehas so completely entered into the feelings of God that his act was equivalent to the act of God. God goes on to say, "Behold, I give to him my covenant of peace; and it shall be to him, and to his descendants after him, the covenant of a perpetual priesthood, because he was jealous for his God, and made atonement for the people of Israel" (25:12).

Phinehas who was jealous with the Lord's jealousy for the purity of the people, and Zadok who was intensely loyal to the Davidic kingship, and Ezra who had elements of both: this is the heritage of the priesthood. It was because of faithful representatives that the line continued; and it is equally true today that because of faithful people of God the work of God is done.

Ezra is called a "scribe" by the Persian king. The word scribe, at that time, had a technical meaning that we must attempt to understand. In David's kingdom the office of scribe was one of political significance. In the New Testament, the scribe was more concerned with the minutiae of legalistic ritual, which probably developed under the aegis of Pharisaism. Just after Ezra's day, the scribe was a member of a professional class that seems to have had a broad field of interests: perhaps something like the European scholar of bygone generations. Jesus ben Sirach describes him in Ecclesiasticus 38:24—39:11. I rather imagine Ezra was a scribe of this kind. The main interest of the scribe was the interpretation of the Law and the Prophets.

Ezra tells us that he requested permission to go from Babylon to Jerusalem: He had heard disconcerting reports about what was happening in Jerusalem in those days, and in accordance with his request, he was sent to Jerusalem by Artaxerxes the king, in order to look into the welfare of the people and to bring about a reform movement.

In order to understand Ezra, we must go back and fit him into his day, for there is no man who is not to a large extent the child of his own time. After we have understood Ezra and have seen what he did of permanent value, then we can learn from him for our own lives. He went to Jerusalem in the seventh year of Artaxerxes (Ezra 7:7). That would have been Artaxerxes I (Longimanus)—Artaxerxes of the Long

Hand—and the date 457 B.C.[4] Cyrus the Great had entered Babylon in 539 B.C. In some ways, Cyrus is unique among political rulers in history. He discontinued the cruel practices of the Semitic tyrants before him, and took pride in the fact that he was a beneficent ruler. He says, "My numerous troops advanced into the heart of Babylon peaceably. . . . In Babylon and all the outlying regions I strove for peace. . . . The yoke which was not honorable I removed from them. Their run-down houses I repaired. . . . The gods . . . I caused to return, their hearts to their places I returned and caused to dwell in an eternal habitation. All their people I assembled and I returned to their habitations."[5] Every report we have shows that Cyrus was as good as his word. One tradition has it that since he could not send the gods of the Jews back to Jerusalem (since they had no idols), he sent the furnishings of the temple instead. His decree permitting the Jews to return to Jerusalem and to rebuild the temple is recorded in Ezra 6:3-5 About fifty thousand persons returned to Jerusalem at that time.

Ezra also tells us a little about the rebuilding of the temple which had been destroyed by the Babylonians in 586; "When the builders laid the foundation of the temple of the Lord, the priests in their vestments came forward with trumpets, and the Levites, the sons of Aspah, with cymbals, to praise the Lord, according to the directions of David king of Israel. . . . But many of the priests and Levites and heads of fathers' houses, old men who had seen the first house, wept with a loud voice when they saw the foundations of this house being laid, though many shouted aloud for joy" (3:10-12). I suppose that we should point out that there were three returns from exile: the first, to which Ezra is referring here, was led by Sheshbazzar, and took place in 538 B.C.; the second was led by Ezra in 457 B.C.; the third by Nehemiah in 445 B.C. Men of twenty who had gone into captivity in 586 B.C. would have been seventy years old when they returned; some of the elders among the returnees could remember the glorious days of the magnificent temple of Solomon, and they looked upon the foundations of the new temple as nothing compared to the old. In Haggai we get something of their attitude and their longing "for the good old days" (Haggai 2:3).

There had been attempts to halt the work. Ezra tells us about an

---

[4] Many scholars today identify him with Artaxerxes II (Mnemon), 404-358 B.C. The best summary of the arguments for the later date, together with replies to them, so far as I know, is in *A Catholic Commentary on Holy Scripture,* pp. 377-378.

[5] Cyrus Cylinder, 24-33.

effort on the part of the Samaritans to put an end to the building. They sent a letter to the king pointing out that this was a rebellious people, and that when they got the city rebuilt, they would stop paying their taxes and revolt, etc., etc. (Ezra 4:11-16). The king was swayed by the letter—he did not realize that he was violating a decree which had already been established by his father—and he halted the work for a while.

Then Haggai and Zechariah came along, and Zerubbabel and Joshua (about 520 B.C.), and under this new leadership and inspiration construction was begun anew. A second effort was made to stop the work, and a full report was forwarded to the Persian king, who by that time was Darius.[6] He searched the records, and found the decree of Cyrus, which read: "In the first year of Cyrus the king, Cyrus the king issued a decree: Concerning the house of God at Jerusalem, let the house be rebuilt, the place where sacrifices are offered and burnt offerings are brought; its height shall be sixty cubits and its breadth sixty cubits. . . . And also let the gold and silver vessels of the house of God, which Nebuchadnezzar took out of the temple that is in Jerusalem . . . be restored . . ." (6:3-5). That allowed them to continue the work.

Now that was about sixty-three years before Ezra's return. The people had spent fifty to seventy years in Babylonia. They had come back to the land and had started the rebuilding of the temple and they had been discouraged, but finally they had completed it. Another sixty years went by, and by that time a cold indifference had settled down over the people. There was even rebellion against the Lord. Some were completely fed up with the whole thing. They had been taken out of their land because they had worshiped God—at least, that was the way they looked at it—then they had been brought *back* into the land, and they had gone through all sorts of opposition and persecution, and they just frankly did not see any sense in the whole performance. Read Malachi to get some of the reaction.

Let us try to find out why. Israel had been taken captive into Babylonia in three stages in 605, 597, and 586; approximately every ten years a group had been taken out of the land, until at last only the poor and the ignorant were left in the land. All of the golden and silver vessels of the temple had been hauled away; everything of any value had been taken, and there was just nothing left but the poor people, and

---

[6] Darius Hystaspis (521-486 B.C.). I often hear the name Darius mispronounced; it should be *dă-rye'-us*.

very little to maintain them. And what had happened to the Hebrew people in Babylonia? They were there for fifty, sixty, or seventy years. The children of those who had been taken into exile from Jerusalem were now old men and old women, and their children had grown up, and their grandchildren and maybe even some of their great grandchildren had been born in Babylon. They had laid out farms and plowed them, they had established their homes; many of them had gone into business.

Ezekiel, the prophet who lived among the exiles, says in his prophecy, "Yet you say, 'The way of the Lord is not just.' Hear now, O house of Israel; Is my way not just? Is it not *your* ways that are not just?" (Ezekiel 18:25). Ezekiel would never had said that if the people had not been complaining against the justice of the Lord. They had reached the point where they thought that God had not treated them fairly. Again, Ezekiel says, "with their lips they show much love, but their heart is set on their gain." The people had moved slowly but surely into a materialistic viewpoint. Then Cyrus came along and said, "All right; you can go back home!" And what did they do? Fifty thousand of them went back; and the rest of them stayed there in Babylon! Why? Because they were more interested in the material things which they had gotten, their businesses and their farms, than they were in going back to the land that God had given to them. And those that had gone back to their land, I suppose, in many cases were the poorer ones. Those who were well established in the land of Babylon probably stayed. There is evidence that even many of the priests did not go back.

That was the situation in Palestine, in Ezra's day. There were those who had not been taken into captivity because they were too poor, because they had no elements of leadership, because the Babylonians just had nothing to fear by leaving them there—possibly fifty to eighty thousand it has been estimated. There were also the returnees who probably were not very successful in business and worldly ventures in Babylon. These two groups started a half-hearted rebuilding program; they started in with a lot of enthusiasm but it died out rather quickly.

Then there were the Samaritans, who wanted to join with them but were rejected. They were not told the exact reason—that their men had intermarried with the Gentiles and that they had not been true to the law of Moses—but they were given another reason: "Cyrus gave us the permission to come back here and rebuild; he did not give *you* any such permission. You would get us into trouble if we brought you in on the deal . . ."; and the Samaritans immediately turned hostile and tried to stop the work.

Further opposition is described in the Book of Nehemiah. In Nehemiah 4 there is the story of the opposition of Sanballat. It became so serious that the Jews, when they were rebuilding the walls, had to designate certain men to carry spears and shields and bows, and those who were carrying burdens were laden in such a way that they worked with one hand and held their weapons with the other; each of the builders on the wall had a sword girded on his side. They had to be ready for an attack from the opposition at all times.

The whole picture is one of a disagreeable time. The people had gotten into such a mess that in 445 B.C., twelve years after Ezra had gone into the land, Nehemiah, who was the cupbearer to the king back in Babylon, asked permission to go to Jerusalem and try to straighten it out. He was made governor of Palestine, in order to do just that.

Ezra's work, briefly, was to renew the spiritual power of Israel. They had almost forgotten their God in their pursuit of worldly gain; they had nearly lost their faith. Ezra called them to build on something more substantial, to rekindle the ancient spiritual fire, and to rebuild the nation. These are the reasons why he went back. He took with him fifteen hundred men; altogether he had not more than five thousand people. They went back at government expense, and took with them the vessels that belonged in the temple.

How do you explain the attitude of the Persian king? May I offer one suggestion? Esther had been the queen of the king who preceded King Artaxerxes known as Ahasuerus or Xerxes. Ahasuerus, according to secular records, was not much of a king. He was more interested in his harem than he was in the welfare of the kingdom. Could it be that Esther had so influenced Ahasuerus that when his able son Artaxerxes came to the throne he demonstrated his gratitude to the Jewish people by giving this privilege to Ezra and to those with him? I do not know; I suppose we shall never know in this life; but it could well be that Esther's influence in that home had brought all this about. I know of no other reason that will explain the gracious treatment of Ezra. When Ezra had finished quoting the king's letter, he said, "Blessed be the Lord, the God of our fathers, who put such a thing as this into the heart of the king, to beautify the house of the Lord which is in Jerusalem, and who extended to me his steadfast love before the king and his counsellors . . ." (Ezra 7:27-28).

Ezra called the people together and read to them from the book of Moses. He had thirteen Levites assist him, to help the people to understand, "and they read from the book, from the law of God, clearly; and gave the sense, so that the people understood the reading"[7] (Nehemiah 8:8). As a result, the people came to realize just how great their sin was, and they confessed their sin and prayed, "Now, therefore, our God, the great and mighty and terrible God, who keepest covenant and steadfast love, let not all the hardship seem little to thee that has come upon us, upon our kings, our princes, our priests, our prophets, our fathers, and all thy people, since the time of the kings of Assyria until this day. Yet thou hast been just in all that has come upon us. . . ." Do you remember how Ezekiel said that the people complained that God was not just? Now at last they realize their sin, and they confess: "Yet thou hast been just in all that has come upon us, for thou hast dealt with us faithfully and we have acted wickedly; our kings, our princes, our priests, and our fathers have not kept thy law or heeded thy commandments and thy warnings which thou didst give them" (Nehemiah 9:32-34).

Ezra made two questionable decisions. He decided at one time to rebuild the walls of Jerusalem. Now he had not been commissioned to do that. Maybe it was a good thing, but it made him at once a target for opposition, and the Samaritans quickly seized the opportunity; they sent a letter back to the king, and they said in effect, "You did not tell him to do this: he is building the walls, and the next thing you know, he will revolt against you." That lowered Ezra's prestige for a while.

His second questionable decision came when he insisted that all of the men of Israel who had married foreign wives should divorce them. There is no question about the danger that they had gotten into by marrying the foreign wives. Nehemiah points it out very well, when he says, "Did not Solomon king of Israel sin on account of such women? Among the many nations there was no king like him, and he was beloved by his God, and God made him king over all Israel; nevertheless foreign women made even him to sin" (Nehemiah 13:25-27). There is no question that there was real danger in the situation. But here were families that had been established for years, and Ezra insisted that *all* of the men divorce their wives. Of course, not all of them went along with it; many of them refused. But this was a questionable decision

[7] According to Jewish interpretation, this was the beginning of the Targums or Aramaic translation of the Hebrew Bible.

on Ezra's part. We never hear any more of him after that; he seems to have lost his prestige and his authority with the people for good. Nehemiah seems to have modified the rule, to prevent future mixed marriages without dissolving the existing ones.

Not only was Ezra there to call the people back to a renewed spiritual life; in the providence of God he was there to do something of even greater value for them and for us. He rewrote the Scriptures. What does that mean? Writing, as we have seen, has a long history. In what form, for example, did Moses write? Did he write in cuneiform (the Amarna letters were so written)? Did he write in Egyptian hieroglyphs (he had been trained in Pharaoh's court)? It is inconceivable that he wrote the Pentateuch in the form in which we have it today: the shapes of the letters, the spelling, and other items, underwent changes in the course of a thousand years. In what form did David's scribe write? He probably used the old "Phoenician" alphabet, similar to the Moabite stone—the letters look quite similar to Greek turned around backwards.[8] Someone, at some time, *must* have put the ancient writings in the later form in which they were preserved for us. Jewish tradition attributes this to Ezra and the men of the Great Synagogue. I understand that to mean that all of the existing Scriptures were cast in "modern" spelling, "square" letters, perhaps with some of the explanatory notes (such as, "and it is there even to this day," etc.), and other editorial elements. Jewish tradition moreover says that it was done by the inspiration of the Lord. I understand that to mean that the Lord inspired Ezra in such a way that the inspiration imparted to the original authors was not destroyed by Ezra's editorial work. But whether my interpretations are accurate or not, it is certain that the Old Testament, as we have it today, came into existence about or not long after the time of Ezra. To whom else shall we attribute it? Where is there any other name of a man of sufficient stature to accomplish the task? Until such can be presented, I am content to say that Ezra was the man raised up of God to bring the restored exiles back to His word, to inaugurate the office of scribe for preservation and interpretation of the Scriptures, and to put into their hands the Old Testament in its final form.

Down through the history of the Hebrew nation, God was using individual men and women. We have studied together fifteen of these great Old Testament personalities. They were great not alone because

---

[8] Actually, Greek letters are Phoenician, turned around.

of great things they did, certainly not because of their sinlessness, and not because they did not make mistakes—every one of them made mistakes, and every one of them was guilty of some sin or other. They were great because they were faithful when God called them. They did the work that He had for them to do.

God does not just work through a nation collectively; He does not just work through a big church or a big Sunday school class collectively; He works *through individual men and women who are faithful in their work.*

Bibliography

BIBLE DICTIONARIES (articles on persons, places, items, etc.)

The Westminster Dictionary of the Bible, edited by John D. Davis, revised and rewritten by Henry Snyder Gehman, Philadelphia: The Westminster Press, 1944. 658 pp., XVI plates. [An excellent Bible Dictionary revised by a careful scholar; if I could have only one, it would be this.]

Harper's Bible Dictionary, edited by Madeleine S. Miller and J. Lane Miller. New York: Harper & Brothers, 1952. 851 pp., XVI plates. [Particularly strong in modern archaeological discoveries; sometimes disappointing in theological or critical views.]

Unger's Bible Dictionary, edited by Merrill F. Unger. Chicago: The Moody Press, 1957. 1192 pp. [Many good articles on Old Testament subjects, from an extremely "Conservative" viewpoint. Although the title page does not show it, much of this dictionary is reprinted without substantial revision form the 1900 edition of C. R. Barnes, *Bible Encyclopaedia.*]

The International Standard Bible Encyclopaedia, edited by James Orr, *et al.,* revised by Melvin Grove Kyle. Chicago: The Howard-Severance Co., 1930. 5 vols. Reprinted by Wm. B. Eerdmans, Grand Rapids, Mich. [An excellent work that deserves careful revision throughout by well-qualified editors and publication in handsome format.]

BIBLE GEOGRAPHIES AND ATLASES

L. H. Grollenberg, *Atlas of the Bible*; translated and edited by Joyce M. H. Reid and H. H. Rowley. New York: Thomas Nelson & Sons, 1956. 165 pages, 37 maps, 408 photographs. [My first choice; a splendid work in every way.]

The Westminster Historical Atlas to the Bible, edited by G. Ernest Wright and Floyd V. Filson. Revised edition. Philadelphia: The Westminster Press, 1956. 130 pp., 18 maps. [A close second to the above; many prefer this. In either case a hearty recommendation!]

George Adam Smith, *The Historical Geography of the Holy Land.* 25th edition. New York and London: Harper & Brothers, 1931. 744 pp., 8 maps. [Long the classical and still the only *historical* geography of the Holy Land. Excellent literary style; careful observations that have withstood the test of sixty-four years. Earlier editions are in places not reliable.]

Denis Baly, *The Geography of the Bible*. New York: Harper & Brothers, 1957. 304 pp., 48 maps and diagrams. [In spite of its subtitle, this is not a historical geography; it is however a valuable physical geography.]

Atlante storico della Bibbia, edited by Paulin Lemaire and Donato Baldi. Turin: Marietti, 1955. 322 pp., 56 maps in text, 13 full-page maps, many photographs. [A beautiful and excellent historical atlas—if you can read Italian.]

ART AND ARCHITECTURE (for pictures and reconstructions)

James B. Pritchard, *The Ancient Near East in Pictures* Relating to the Old Testament. Princeton: Princeton University Press, 1954. 351 pp., 769 plates. [A magnificent work covering just about everything significant as defined in the title.]

Henri Frankfort, *The Art and Architecture of the Ancient Orient*. (The Pelican History of Art.) Baltimore: Penguin Books, 1954. 279 pp., 192 plates. [A fine work, chiefly on Mesopotamian art, with Asia Minor, the Levant, and Persia as "Peripheral Regions," but without Egypt.]

Heinrich Schäfer and Walter Andrae, *Die Kunst des alten Orients*. (Propyläen-Kunstgeschichte, 2). 3d edition. Berlin: Propyläen-Verlag, 1925. 762 pp. (616 of which are pictures), XXXII plates (some of which are in color). [Excellent coverage, including Egypt. The German text is simply a descriptive catalog of the pictures.]

Christiane Desroches-Noblecourt, *Le style égyptien*. (Arts, styles et techniques.) Paris: Librairie Larousse, 1946. 220 pp., 64 plates. [Popular, inexpensive, and reliable for an introduction to Egyptian art and architecture.]

ARCHAEOLOGY

G. Ernest Wright, *Biblical Archaeology*. Philadelphia: The Westminster Press, 1957. 288 pp. [A beautifully produced work, written by a foremost expert in the subject.]

William F. Albright, *The Archaeology of Palestine* (Pelican Books, A199.) Revised edition. Baltimore: Penguin Books, 1954. 271 pp., 30 plates. [An excellent, inexpensive work by the dean of American archaeologists.]

J. A. Thompson, *Archaeology and the Old Testament*. (A Pathway Book.) Grand Rapids: Wm. B. Eerdmans Publishing Co., 1957. 121 pp. [Brief, simply told, reliable.]

Merrill F. Unger, *Archeology and the Old Testament*. Grand Rapids: Zondervan Publishing House, 1954. 339 pp. [An excellent selection of material integrated with Biblical history. At times the author lets his convictions overshadow the evidence.]

Seton Lloyd. *Foundations in the Dust*. (Pelican Books, A336.) Baltimore: Penguin Books, 1955. 256 pp. [Originally published in 1947; a reliable and interesting account of Mesopotamian archaeology.]

Seton Lloyd, *Early Anatolia*. (Pelican Books, A354). Baltimore: Penguin Books, 1956. 231 pp., 32 plates. [A most interesting work. I carried it on 6,000 miles of study throughout Turkey and can vouch for its reliability.]

Millar Burrows, *What Mean These Stones?* (Living Age Books, 7.) New York: Meridian Books, 1957. 306 pp. [Originally published in 1941; written by a careful and well-qualified scholar.]

Chester Charlton McCown, *The Ladder of Progress in Palestine*. New York: Harper & Brothers, 1943. 387 pp. [A most stimulating work with a selected bibliography.]

CHRONOLOGY

Robert W. Ehrich, ed., *Relative Chronologies in Old World Archeology*. Chicago: University of Chicago Press, 1954. 154 pp. [Experts in each area present the basic materials for a universal chronology. The work is difficult —but necessary!]

P. van der Meer, *The Chronology of Ancient Western Asia and Egypt*. 2d revised edition. Leiden: E. J. Brill, 1955. 95 pp. [Again, difficult, but necessary.]

Edwin R. Thiele, *The Mysterious Numbers of the Hebrew Kings*. Chicago: The University of Chicago Press, 1951. 298 pp. [The author has succeeded in harmonizing the chronologies of the kings of Israel and Judah to the satisfaction of most scholars. No one working in the field can ignore this book.]

THE ANCIENT NEAR EAST

Jack Finegan, *Light from the Ancient Past*. Princeton: Princeton University Press, 1946. 500 pp., 204 plates. [A carefully written, thoroughly documented account of the archaeological and historical matters that pertain to the Biblical record.]

H. R. Hall, *The Ancient History of the Near East*. Eleventh edition. London: Methuen & Co., 1950. 620 pp., 33 plates. [First edition 1913; a standard reference work.]

Sabatino Moscati, *Ancient Semitic Civilizations*. London: Elek Books, 1957. 254 pp. [A delightful and valuable work by a man who writes equally well in several languages.]

Cyrus H. Gordon, *The Living Past*. New York: The John Day Company, 1941. 232 pp., 27 plates. [A popularized treatment of the results of archaeology by an excellent scholar.]

Cyrus H. Gordon, *Introduction to Old Testament Times*. Ventnor, N. J.: Ventnor Publishers, 1953. 312 pp. [A delightful presentation of the background of the Old Testament reconstructed from modern historical research.]

V. Gordon Childe, *What Happened in History*. (Pelican Books, A108.) Baltimore: Penguin Books, 1954. 288 pp. [First published in 1942, revised after several printings. A fascinating survey of man from Palaeolithic savagery to the end of the ancient world.]

William F. Albright, *From the Stone Age to Christianity*. Second edition. Baltimore: Johns Hopkins Press, 1957. 432 pp. [Since it first appeared in 1940, this has been recognized as a most important work. It is not easy reading.]

James B. Pritchard, editor, *Ancient Near Eastern Texts* Relating to the Old Testament. Second edition. Princeton: Princeton University Press, 1955. 544 pp. [This volume contains practically all of the relevant texts that throw light on the Old Testament, translated by world-renowned experts in each field, well annotated.]

OLD TESTAMENT HISTORY

W. O. E. Oesterley and T. H. Robinson, *A History of Israel*. Oxford: Clarendon Press, 1932. 2 vols. [Vol. I, by Robinson, covers the period from the Exodus to the Fall of Jerusalem, 586 B.C. (496 pp.); Vol. II, by Oesterley, from the Fall of Jerusalem to the Bar-Kokhba Revolt, A.D. 135 (516 pp.). The work follows the critical viewpoint, but has a wealth of valuable material.]

Paul Heinisch, *History of the Old Testament,* translated by William Heidt. Collegeville, Minn.: Liturgical Press, 1952. 492 pp. [Revised from the German edition of 1949, this Roman Catholic work is both rich and reverent. As a general rule, Roman Catholic works do not follow the extremes of critical scholarship. This work has a vast number of excellent references.]

Werner Keller, *The Bible as History;* Archaeology Confirms the Book of Books; translated by William Neil. London: Hodder & Stoughton, 1956. 429

pp. [Well told in understandable language, with a wealth of material. One gets the impression at times that in his desire to support the subtitle of his book, he has not presented all sides of some questions.]

THE MODERN ATTEMPT AT SYNTHESIS

H. H. Rowley, *The Re-discovery of the Old Testament.* London: James Clarke & Co., 1945. 224 pp. [Stimulating.]

G. Ernest Wright, *The Old Testament Against its Environment.* (Studies in Biblical Theology, 2.) London: SCM Press, 1950. 116 pp. [A work that is quoted repeatedly.]

H. H. Rowley, editor, *The Old Testament and Modern Study.* Oxford: Clarendon Press, 1951. 405 pp. [Twelve outstanding scholars discuss the impact of modern discovery upon the various fields of Old Testament study. An extremely significant book, worth repeated careful reading, with excellent bibliographies.]

Quite a few additional pertinent titles are listed, with comments, in my *Basic Semitic Bibliography* (Wheaton, Ill.: Van Kampen Press, 1950; 56 pp.). Other titles are sprinkled in the footnotes of the preceding pages. And I am fully aware that I have omitted many books of outstanding merit, not a few of which I use constantly. But there are space limitations which I must observe.

Index